The Vision Bold

The Vision Bold

An Illustrated History of the Seventh-day Adventist Philosophy of Health

Editors: WARREN L. JOHNS, RICHARD H. UTT

Introduction: GODFREY T. ANDERSON
Contributing Authors: OLIVER L. JACQUES,
RICHARD B. LEWIS, W. FREDERICK NORWOOD,
FLOYD O. RITTENHOUSE,
RICHARD W. SCHWARZ, ERIC WERE

REVIEW AND HERALD PUBLISHING ASSOCIATION, WASHINGTON, D.C. 20012

CREDITS

Project Sponsors
DELMER D. FJARLI, M.D., JAMES W.
WHITE, M.D., H. E. HEIN, KARL YARED,
LEWIS E. NIERMEYER, HAROLD JAMES, M.D.,
L. ALBERT LEWIS

Art Director and Design
RON KWIEK

Design Consultant
HARRY KNOX

Color Photography
JIM BURTNETT
HENRY RASMUSSEN
RICK JOHNS
ROBERT WHEELER

Copyright © 1977 by Review and Herald Publishing Association. All rights reserved. Library of Congress Catalog Card No. 77-71632. Printed in the United States of America.

ELMSHAVEN
The Little Elderly Lady of Elmshaven ... 10
Pills, Potions, Purges, and Prussic Acid ... 22

BATTLE CREEK
Will Success Spoil John Kellogg? ... 38
Granola, Postum, Corn Flakes, and Peanut Butter ... 74
"That's A Wonderful Bargain, but We Haven't A Cent" ... 94

WESTWARD
Another Kellogg, Another San ... 108
Where Koala Bears Munched Gum-Tree Leaves ... 126
God Will Give the Thirsty Elephant A Drink ... 146
What Makes Burden Borrow? ... 160

LOMA LINDA
The Resurrection of Lonesome Linda ... 174
"They Have Gone and Done What I Told Them Not To" ... 188

Postscript ... 202
Biographical Sketches ... 204
Index ... 206

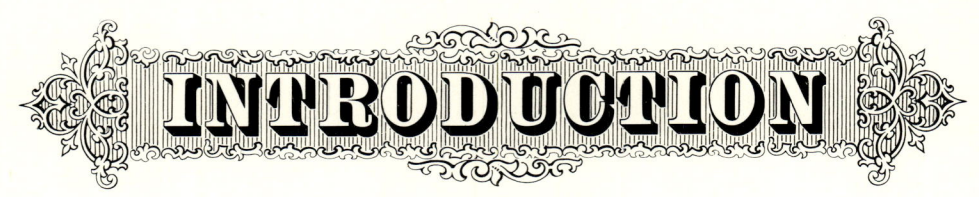

Editors Warren L. Johns and Richard H. Utt,
with Godfrey T. Anderson, Former President of Loma Linda University,
at Elmshaven, California

This volume is a fascinating human-interest story of the beginnings of the Seventh-day Adventist philosophy of health and the establishment of the church's early health centers. The institutions whose history is given here extended from mid-America to California and to distant Australia and New Zealand. The story is told against the background of the medical milieu of the nineteenth and early twentieth centuries. It portrays the developing interest in "natural remedies," including the health-food emphasis which led to a profitable new industry at Battle Creek and elsewhere in America and Australia. Foremost among the changes introduced along this line were the prepared breakfast foods which revolutionized the dietary habits of millions.

This book attempts to give back to the history of pioneer Seventh-day Adventist medical institutions some of the flavor and piquancy which have often been missed heretofore. The impressive collection of nearly 300 photographs, drawings, and portraits which accompany the text will cause long-forgotten people, places, and events to live again in our minds and consciences.

The names which stand out in the outline of the church's medical work are here fleshed out into real people who had problems and wrestled with them, who had doubts and vanquished them, who gave their time and effort in a generosity almost unbelievable today, when so much less is required or even expected of our workers—at least in prosperous America.

In and out of the narrative appear the names of such colorful persons as John and Will Kellogg, David and Mary Paulson, John Burden, and Percy Magan, who with many others figure prominently in the account. Involved in most aspects of the story was Ellen White, who with foresight and divine direction gave the right counsel at the proper time to assure the success of one enterprise after another.

The record prods us to look at ourselves as well as our predecessors in the work of the church. Their utter dedication and zest for giving humble our more moderate efforts. At the same time, we can appreciate the dilemmas posed by different viewpoints and hostile circumstances. The impact of the Kellogg brothers on the health program of the church is given credit long overdue—recognition we have sometimes neglected to give because of doctrinal differences.

Through it all we see the guidance of God as projected by the little lady from Elmshaven. At strategic moments in the development of our medical work, this remarkable woman gave the encouragement and wise counsel needed to keep the program balanced and moving forward. We are led to conclude that when God needs special people for special tasks He is always able to find them.

This book is calculated to provide antibodies in the spiritual blood of the church to combat the toxins of materialism and greed which are such a threat to humankind everywhere. To read it is a refreshing experience which inspires a rebirth of hope for the future.

GODFREY T. ANDERSON

ELMSHAVEN

THE LITTLE ELDERLY LADY OF

ELMSHAVEN

WHEN
SHE
SPOKE, THE
"LEADING BRETHREN"
PAID
ATTENTION

The scene could hardly be more improbable: an elderly five-foot-two woman engaged in heated conference with a roomful of male educators and administrators on the subject of wage scales for physicians. The fact that she is even present at such a sensitive policy session is remarkable. The administrators disagree sharply, but it is her advice that prevails. Unquestionably, the last word is hers.

The confrontation is prompted by an issue as current as life in a space lab. The question of remuneration for physicians and members of other health-related professions still confronts educators and military and civil-service institutions. Consumer groups and legislators at state and national levels still wrestle with the issue as they seek to give form to adequate systems for the delivery of health-care services.

But this is not 1975, nor is the encounter an incident in the women's liberation movement. The year is 1913, and the lone female at the

meeting is Ellen White, aged eighty-five. She and they are dealing with problems incident to the operation of a new and struggling medical school on a farm at Loma Linda, in southern California.

Her disposition of the argument says something about the character of the school and those who operate it. In response to claims that physicians deserve special consideration because they are "more skilled, work harder, and save lives," Ellen White says No. Stenographic transcripts of the conference provide no evidence of senility, nor is there any discernible lack of either insight or courage in her comments. She suggests that physicians' wages may have to be reduced rather than increased. "It is not advisable," she says, "to pay one man considerably more than another doing similar work. . . . It is of no use for us to think that we can offer a successful worker a high wage simply because he may demand it." She points out that selfishness will disrupt the institutional harmony vital to the achievement of its objectives, which must remain distinctly Christian and worldwide in scope.

The session held at Elmshaven, her home in Napa County, north of San Francisco, is the most recent of conferences on this and other subjects over a period of years. What is noteworthy is the fact that these men return to southern California and follow her counsel!

The fledgling school was to become the educational hub of a world complex of Christian clinics and hospitals operated by Seventh-day Adventists, a small but widely dispersed denomination in the reformation-evangelical tradition.

The Adventists were distinguished by their belief in the imminent return of Christ and by their observance of the seventh-day Sabbath. In short, they rested on Saturday rather than Sunday, and they proposed to carry their message of Christ's soon return to every nation on earth. Ellen White had been at the heart of the movement from its inception. While she did not claim the title "prophetess," those who knew her best were convinced that she possessed the gift of prophecy. She also possessed an arsenal of other gifts. She was a prodigious writer and a popular and effective speaker. She had inspired and promoted educational and health institutions in many places. As if this were not enough, she set the pace for theological development of the Advent movement, and was a principal interpreter of Adventist philosophy over a period of nearly seventy years. Her book *Steps to Christ* was to become a classic interpretation of the Christian experience to people of many nationalities and faiths.

A most productive period of Ellen White's career began at the turn of the century, thirteen years prior to the confrontation mentioned above. She had just returned from a nine-year visit to Australia and New Zealand where she had, at the request of church leaders, helped organize educational and medical institutions, giving the church areas of influence in new lands. Though loath to leave the free and lively Australians, she had done so because of a pervasive unrest developing within the church and its medical work in the United States. She believed that certain organizational and policy trends were inhibiting progress and the achievement of a truly Christian witness.

Returning to the States, she determined to limit her involvement to writing and to matters of long-range planning and policy. At seventy-two, she felt too old to become entangled in the immediate problems of any place or institution. She especially wished to avoid close involvement at Battle Creek, Michigan, world headquarters of the church and site of the Battle Creek Sanitarium, the famous medical center operated by Seventh-day Adventists.

To the surprise of many and the dismay of some, Ellen White decided to purchase as her home and headquarters a country estate in a valley surrounded by the hills of Napa County, California. Living a week's travel away from Battle Creek, she was accessible to the church leadership to discuss any matters justifying their trip. She would also live in closer proximity to church activities in the West, where the work was newer and more flexible than in the East.

The estate included some acres of vineyards, orchards, farmlands, and timbered hills. A stream ran through the property. A commodious home on a pleasant knoll was available complete with furnishings, supplies, horses, and carriages. She and her domestic and editorial staffs could resume work with a minimum of inconvenience. The idyllic surroundings promised her the serenity and aesthetic inspiration essential to long-range planning and creative writing. "Elmshaven," as she named her new home, was three miles from a railway station at the small town of Saint Helena. It was to become a unique center of influence in the Adventist world.

America during the halcyon years before World War I was virile and opportunistic, with

expectations of unrivaled greatness. The industrial age flowered. Railways had opened up the Western plains, along with the wealth and romance of California. The Panama Canal, soon to be completed, would facilitate commercial ties between East and West Coasts, and trade with the Orient. Wars with Spain and Mexico, as unnecessary and trivial as they now seem, provided the burgeoning nation with ego-building muscle flexing and a certain arrogance.

Overseas, the British Empire provided economic stability and beneficent government to great segments of mankind. Kaiser Wilhelm's Germany was achieving new standards of culture and industry. The French were stabilizing their republic, and Russia, under the faltering leadership of Czar Nicholas, was recovering from a humbling encounter with the Japanese navy. Europe's major powers had agreed on joint exploitation of China, and the Boers in South Africa had submitted to the honor and other benefits of British sovereignty. The victorious English, along with an international horde of fortune seekers, were digging deep holes in the ground at Kimberley.

Philosophers and not a few religionists believed that man's golden age had come. Warfare had been shown to be pointless and unnecessary, and the Kellogg-Briand Treaty made the concept official. To be sure, a few ragtail radicals such as Marx and Engels played with alternate philosophies. But most people knew that science and industry plus education and enlightenment would save the world. Man had, to the relief of thoughtful people, at last grown up. And he had gained such insights! Many educators and clergy, except of course for the Billy Sunday breed of evangelists, were making peace with Charles Darwin and his theories.

Man's progress apparently knew no limits. During these years an Italian named Guglielmo Marconi established trans-Atlantic wireless service. Commander Robert E. Peary reached the North Pole, and Detroit's Henry Ford was driving a horseless carriage. Thomas Edison's electric lights were taken for granted in America's cities and even in some rural areas. Even ordinary people were getting telephones. Two brothers from Ohio managed to create a flying machine, though few saw anything useful in the stunt.

Such news-world giants as Adolph Ochs, William Randolph Hearst, and William Allan White expanded practically everyone's minds with detailed international information. *The Saturday Evening Post, Harper's, Frank Leslie's Illustrated Newspaper*, and *Ladies' Home Journal* added to the enlightenment while promoting Castoria, Lydia Pinkham's Female Compound, and Dr. Williams' Pink Pills for Pale People. "It floats," "Do you know U NEED A biscuit?" and "His Master's Voice" appeared in publications everywhere.

A one-time slave, George Washington Carver, explored new horizons for Southern agriculture. Luther Burbank developed new strains of fruit trees. An off-beat Vienna physician, Sigmund Freud, wrote "Jokes and Their Relation to the Unconscious" and "Three Essays on the Theory of Sexuality." Parents rewarded their offspring for good conduct with a stick of Wrigley's chewing gum, and most families owned a bicycle or two. By 1900, population in the United States had passed the 75 million mark, up 13 million from a decade before.

One would suppose that in an age witnessing such yeasty ferment, churches in general, and Adventism in particular, would thrive. This was not necessarily so. While Seventh-day Adventists pushed ahead energetically in various ways and places, Ellen White saw their development as unsatisfactory, with deficiencies both in character and influence. If the church was to justify its existence, its members must achieve higher levels of godliness, enlarge their vision of a world task, and enter into a Christian ministry designed to show the divine love in unmistakably personal terms. For many years she had seen in the ministry of healing a unique method of advancing Christ's kingdom on earth. The church had in its medical institutions at Battle Creek and elsewhere a strong and apparently successful work.

However, Dr. John Harvey Kellogg, and many with him, had begun to think of the medical missionary work, as they called it, essentially as a humanitarian program designed to bring health and betterment to mankind. Though they may not have realized it, this line of work had to them become an end in itself.

The clergy, on the other hand, were beginning to suspect that the medical branch of the work was getting out of hand, overshadowing other forms of ministry. They considered some of Dr. Kellogg's health ideas extreme.

Ellen White and her staff had hardly settled themselves in their new home at Elmshaven when the church's leaders urged her to attend a General Conference session in Battle Creek scheduled for April, 1901. While she felt compelled to go because of her concern for the church's unsettled condition, at seventy-three she was tired and wished to devote her time to writing. She had never been of robust health. The long journey seemed formidable, but less so than the trends that were jeopardizing the world mission of Seventh-day Adventists. Needed reforms fell into several categories. Spiritual revival must be accompanied by a realignment of priorities. Church authority must be decentralized. Decisions customarily made in Battle Creek might better be made at local or regional levels. The church's fragmented programs in education, missions, and health should be unified organizationally.

A stronger, more distinctive system of education for Adventist youth must be developed. To achieve this, new schools and colleges would have to be built. Some might have to be moved. The medical missionary work should not only be linked more closely to the church; it must in a special sense *be* the church fulfilling its healing ministry in the footsteps of Christ Himself.

History has demonstrated that it is next to impossible for churches, governments, or other organizations to achieve reform from within. As clearly as the need for reform may be recognized,

Ellen G. White at Elmshaven in 1914, the year before her death. Front row, left to right: Dores E. Robinson, Editor; R. W. Munson, Visitor; Mrs. White; W. C. White; Clarence C. Crisler, Chief Secretary. Second row: Mr. Bee; Maggie Hare Bee, Secretary; Mary Stewart, Editor; Paul Mason, Accountant; Arthur W. Spalding, Writer; Helen Graham, Stenographer; Tessie Woodbury, Housekeeper; A. Carter, Janitor; Mae Wailing, Mrs. White's niece; Effie James, Stenographer.

once traditions and patterns have been established, change comes hard if at all. This is especially true if proven policies and procedures can be shown to be "successful," and is preeminently true of religious organizations. Traditions and doctrine are often confused, and change of any sort is viewed as heresy.

Ellen White, a woman in a society that did not allow females to vote, determined to initiate a reform and turn around an international religious movement. To achieve this, members as well as leaders would need to be reeducated. New and broader philosophies would have to be developed and communicated. Every branch of the church's work must be seen in a new light. The medical missionary work, the line of endeavor many considered most successful, would, if the objectives as she saw them were to be met, have to undergo the most radical transformation.

Battle lines for a destructive conflict and possible rift had been established. The clergy rallied in opposition to the forces of Dr. John Harvey Kellogg, whose international medical missionary and benevolent association represented a working force of over 2,000 professional and administrative people. Other elements of the church combined boasted only 1,500 full-time employees.

Though the work of the church was directed mainly from its General Conference headquarters in Battle Creek, the denomination had fragmented its ministries. The medical missionary work had its own governing board, led by Dr. Kellogg. Another independent group directed the Sabbath School program. Another organization, the Foreign Mission Board, administered overseas mission programs. The International Tract Society focused on home missions. The National Religious Liberty Association functioned independently, and schools and colleges were largely on their own. The publishing work had virtually become a law unto itself.

In short, the General Conference, governed by a handful of men, had grown quite ineffective. It could not provide progressive guidance to a movement that had spread over North America and to Europe, Africa, the Orient, and Australia.

Though Ellen White had lived overseas, her influence through her writings had grown among the church members. Her position at the conference relative to the rivalry between the two major ministries was the subject of considerable speculation. A number of ministers were therefore shaken when they learned that she and her staff had accepted Dr. Kellogg's invitation to stay in his large Battle Creek residence. Many discerning delegates saw only chaos and decay ahead for the church as a whole.

Deeply perplexed herself, Mrs. White had decided to say little during the first days of the conference. She was, however, invited to attend a pre-session meeting of church leaders. Much to her surprise, they immediately called upon her to speak. "I didn't expect to lead out in this meeting," she replied. "I thought I would let you lead out, and then, if I had anything to say, I would say it."

"Well, it seems to me," the chairman said, "that we have said about as much as we wish until we have heard from you."

Ellen White came quickly to the point. "I would prefer not to speak today, though not because I have nothing to say. I have something to say." She then identified with absolute candor organizational conditions and attitudes that were impeding progress. She emphasized the need for reorganization so that more than a few would be involved in making decisions. "The management . . . must be entirely changed, newly organized. To have the conference pass on and close as the [other] conferences have done, with the same

RICK JOHNS

manipulating, and with the very same tone and the same order—God forbid! God forbid, brethren! God calls for a change!"

She called for new ideas and broader plans, for renewed dedication and willingness to sacrifice. She branded as "contemptible in the sight of God, contemptible" those who demanded higher wages for themselves. She called for men to stand as true to principle as the needle to the pole, and referred to "sharp dealings" which actually resulted in losses instead of gains. Some became anxious when she called for a better response to the health-reform efforts of Dr. Kellogg. She said that God did not intend the medi-

cal work to be separated from the gospel work.

The conference convened the next morning with President G. A. Irwin presiding. He gave his report and surrendered the work of his office to the conference. "The conference is now formally opened. What is your pleasure?" he said.

Ellen White, who had hesitated to speak the day before at the pre-session meeting, left her seat in the audience and pressed toward the pulpit. She spoke for an hour, appealing to the delegates to practice the truth as well as preach it, and to work for reorganization. "What we want now is a reorganization. We want to begin at the foundation, and to build upon a different principle." She called for broad participation in the church's decision-making. In the past, the small General Conference committee in Battle Creek had made most decisions. "That these men should stand in a sacred place, to be as the voice of God to the people, as we once believed the General Conference to be—that is past," she exclaimed.

When she had finished her call for spiritual and organizational conversion, President Irwin said he was glad such a call came at the beginning of the session. Arthur Daniells, a forty-three-year-old American delegate from Australia, moved that "all previously laid plans—all usual rules and precedents for arranging and transacting the business of the conference be suspended," and that a committee representing all elements of the church plan for the work of the conference.

Daniells predicted that if delegates would "step out boldly to follow the light which God gives us, whether we can see clear through to the end or not, if we walk in the light we have, go just as far as we can today, God will give us further light, and He will bring us out of bondage into glorious liberty."

When the delegates hesitated to support such an unprecedented proposal, Mrs. White stood and urged that no one block the motion. The chair put the matter to the vote, and it carried unanimously. Thus did this remarkable old lady

Mrs. Grace Jacques, granddaughter of Ellen White, welcomes visitors to Elmshaven.

with no official role beyond that of a delegate initiate a revolution in an otherwise structured conference session.

For three weeks, in an atmosphere that must be described as broadly participative, delegates hammered out decisions altering the organization of the church. They established conferences in major zones throughout the world, with authority to make most of their own administrative decisions. They merged the independent associations with the church administrations at union and General Conference levels, and laid the foundation to enlarge it still more two years later, including leaders from each of the newly formed departments. The powerful medical work was to have its men on the General Conference committee, which would include six representatives from the medical missionary organization. Other precipitous changes followed. Early one morning Ellen White asked Percy T. Magan, vigorous dean of the college at Battle Creek, to visit her. She discussed with him influences at Battle Creek that were impeding development of the unique educational program needed to prepare Adventist youth for effective service. Following a report by Magan that morning, she asked for the floor and urged that the time had come to move the educational center to a new location. As traumatic as this proposal was, each committee and the conference at large voted to move the college. It was reestablished the following autumn at Berrien Springs, ninety miles away.

At a final meeting, at which leaders and delegates expressed their acceptance of the new organization, Ellen White called for unity and cooperation between health workers and ministers.

Conference delegates chose Arthur G. Daniells as leader of the General Conference. Daniells, a man of proven ability, had worked closely with Mrs. White in Australia. Son of a physician who died on a Civil War battlefield, Daniells was to lead the church through twenty-one years of phenomenal growth throughout the world.

Scenes from Elmshaven. Above, Richard Utt interviews Arthur White and Grace White Jacques, grandson and granddaughter of Ellen G. White.

The Vision Bold

TO
VISIT
ELMSHAVEN
IS TO SEE
AND FEEL ANOTHER
ERA

IT IS TO SENSE,
TO APPRECIATE ANEW,
A GREAT LEGACY
OF
FAITH

The Vision Bold

PILLS POTIONS PURGES & PRUSSIC ACID

A DISENCHANTED LOOK AT THE HEALING ARTS AS PRACTICED A CENTURY OR MORE AGO

ike so many Easterners, John Preston Kellogg, a young Massachusetts broommaker, grew restless. He knew that Kelloggs had lived on the Connecticut River across from Northampton for four or five generations, but one day in 1834 he saw a public notice at the community trading center and decided to head westward. The notice described lush green Michigan land untouched by hoe or plow, available for a dollar or so an acre.

Letters from Lansing Dickinson, a friend who had already gone west, strengthened his resolve. Selling his business, Kellogg loaded his household goods on a wagon with his wife, Mary, and two small sons, Merritt and Smith Moses, and headed west.

With all their possessions on the small wagon, the pioneer family rode and walked to Albany, New York, where they boarded a horse-drawn barge on the Erie Canal. Opened in 1825, this waterway linked Eastern communities with the great lakes. Daily steamboats between Buffalo and Detroit, a trading post with a population of 5,000, provided access to the almost impenetrable woodlands of Michigan.

Purchasing another team and wagon in Detroit, the Kelloggs drove on sandy roads through dark forests up the coast until they came to "Dickinson's Settlement" near today's Flint. Declining to purchase what is now downtown Flint for $2,000 because of the "congestion" (twelve families in a fourteen-mile radius), John pushed to the periphery where he purchased 320 acres for $400.

Chippewa Indians still inhabited the dense forests. John and Mary lived at first in a temporary shelter and somehow survived the Michigan winter. When weather and health permitted, they cleared acreage of its giant oak, hickory, ash, and maple trees. They had an inexhaustible supply of white pine, so useful in building log cabins. Before the first snowfall of the second winter, John had built an 18 x 24-foot cabin which boasted three rooms below with two small bedrooms in the loft.

The next few years were not easy. Mary bore her husband three more children. Both John and Mary were ill much of the time. She had what the frontier doctor called "consumption." He prescribed bleeding and the inhalation of resin fumes created by sprinkling resin over a shovel of live coals. The smoke induced coughing which in turn caused hemorrhaging, which was thought to be useful. She died soon after the birth of her fifth child.

Kellogg had not gotten rich! He had cleared some land, but crops were meager. He had lost his wife and was hopelessly in debt, thanks to the failure of a bank he and two neighbors had founded. He and the children frequently lay sick. With the help of Merritt, who was ten, he cared for the smaller children through the winter. Several times he asked Ann Stanley, a young schoolteacher in the village of Threadville, ten miles away, to help with the children. She could not leave her teaching.

When John's eyes became seriously infected, the country doctor applied a wasp sting to the back of his neck "to draw out the blood." The children were purged, bled, vomited, and blistered when ill.

One morning in March, after a desperate winter, Kellogg dressed and fed the children, told them not to fall into the fire, hitched up his horses, and headed for Threadville.

When school was out, he made a last appeal to Ann to help with the children. She replied that she couldn't see fit to leave her school.

"Will you come as my wife?" he pleaded.

"As your wife, I will go," she said. She left her school and accompanied him.

The young schoolmarm made an excellent wife and mother, and she knew something about farming. Urging John to keep sheep to provide wool for the children's clothes, she also persuaded him to plant clover instead of swamp grass. The cattle and horses did better. The soil improved, and they found a ready market for clover seed.

Harvesting and threshing the clover by hand, they sold enough seed at $5 a bushel to pay off the $1,000 bank debt with 10 percent interest. They also built a commodious home and had enough left for a two-seated light spring wagon. In time Ann bore her husband twelve children. She named her fifth John Harvey.

By 1849 John and Ann had made several moves westward, each time developing a new farm. Their last move was to Tyrone Township near Battle Creek. Late in the summer of that year, two-year-old Emma became sick. Ann thought the child had inflammation of the lungs. A physician from Hartland Center treated the child for worms. She died in convulsions after

Ann Stanley Kellogg and John Preston Kellogg, staunch pioneers of Adventism in early Battle Creek. Two of their sons became famous.

The Vision Bold

BETTMANN ARCHIVE

Physicians were Jacks-of-all-trades, and not above advertising the fact. This seventeenth-century English physician's shingle, of carved wood and painted various colors, shows him standing erect, confident, with his medicines behind him. In the panel above, the doctor stands at a patient's bedside holding a urine glass. Upper left, he performs bloodletting. Below, a person with a satisfied air, due no doubt to the skill of the doctor, is having a leg amputated. In the lowest niche the doctor performs the office of dentist, extracting a tooth. Upper right, he seems to be making a chiropractic adjustment. Middle right, he treats a woman's breast. The lower right panel is not clear. The physician appears to have his hand in the patient's pocket, but perhaps he is exerting pressure on a man's lumbar muscles.

Physicians in consultation. A lithograph by L. Boilly. BETTMANN ARCHIVE

the purging. The Kelloggs had more than their share of frontier medicine, and they were bitter.

In those days little was known about health or the causes and treatment of disease. Bleeding and drugging were considered basic therapeutic methodologies.

George Washington, in a short illness which proved fatal, had suffered both bleeding and drugging. Complaining of a sore throat and fever, he was bled, purged, and blistered to death.

Dr. Gallup, a New England man of medicine, believing most diseases to be inflammatory in nature, held that bleeding was the sovereign remedy. It had been observed that no matter how high the fever, it would subside if the patient was bled enough!

Here is a typical case reported by John Ferriar, M.D., in *Medical Histories and Reflections*. The patient: James Johnson, 23. Complaint: dropsy. August 15, 1810. "After trying some other diuretics, took the *infusorum nicotianoe* in the quantity of eighty drops in twenty-four hours, for three days together." This "produced sickness," but did not produce the desired effect. "Fifteen grains of jalap and two drachms of cream of tartar given at bedtime, vomited him briskly, and reduced the swellings for a time." However, strange to say, "the most powerful diuretics given in large doses" proved ineffective.

Toward the end of September he was given, "after a gradual augmentation," one hundred and twenty of the tonic pills in one day. This treatment brought on a "degree of vertigo," and the pills were therefore omitted and some wine prescribed. The doctor also ordered thirty drops of *spiritus aetheris vitriolici* to be given four times a day. The day after this, "pain in the bowels and a diarrhea came on," so "the vitriolic spirit was omitted." "Opiates and astringents were now given, but with little success."

On the fifth of November the patient was ordered three grains of digitalis, which on the seventh were augmented to four. By this time the patient was desirous of "returning to his native air" and dismissed from the infirmary before there was time to experience the effect of the new course of drugging. Though much relieved, according to the physician, he deemed that Mr. Johnson had "little prospect of being ultimately cured."

Medical education was not limited to centers of learning at Philadelphia, Boston, or New York. Scores of schools sprang up offering M.D. degrees in from six to nine months. While as early as 1760 New York had enacted a law requiring practitioners of medicine and surgery to be examined and licensed, anyone with an assortment of drugs and a yen to try his hand at healing could make his way as a physician. The American Medical Association, founded in 1847, had no power to regulate medical education or practice.

Apothecaries, as druggists were called, could diagnose illness and prescribe and sell any medicine or drug—and anyone could be an apothecary. They could choose from an astonishing variety of exotic drugs.

Mercury was a favorite "cure" for syphilis. Patients were dosed internally and rubbed with it externally until saliva flowed from their mouths in a stream and their teeth loosened.

Anyone professing illness was purged with calomel. Tartar emetic and a salt of antimony were used to vomit and purge.

Earlier, crocodile manure had been valued throughout Europe as a powerful remedy. A French dentist named Fauchard had found urine useful as a mouthwash to cure toothache. Cotton Mather of New England had used crushed sow bugs and crushed body lice with "excellent results" in treating the sick.

The first edition of *Encyclopedia Britannica* extolled the virtues of usnea. This was an official drug in the pharmacopeia until the early part of the nineteenth century and was carried in all apothecary shops. Usnea is a moss or mold, and sometimes this was scraped from the skull of a criminal who had been hanged in chains. The substance was taken internally. "Cures" were also achieved by rubbing one's body with a piece of rope used in hanging a criminal.

When Dr. Robert Boyle expurgated the pharmacopeia of various questionable remedies, he retained the sole of an old shoe, "worn by some man that walked much." Ground up, this was taken internally for dysentery.

Copper sulphate or blue vitriol had long been famous. In England they called it "sympathetic powder." Supposedly, it induced healing.

The potato was first used as a medicine and rivaled unicorn or rhinoceros horn as an aphrodisiac. Gold dissolved in acid had great curative powers.

Homeopathy was widely practiced, especially in England. Hahnemann, a nineteenth-century physician, based a popular type of homeopathy on the "signature" principle. Since the nutmeg looks like the brain, he said, it should be used for diseases of the brain. A flower with a small black spot should be used in treating the eyes.

The homeopaths generally killed fewer people than the allopaths, who were more in number and who used massive doses of drugs. It was said that the patients of the homeopaths died of the disease, while those of the allopaths died of the cure.

Some practitioners were quacks, though quite harmless. Dr. James Graham had an institution known as "Temple of Health" in London. It offered the "celestial bed." For fifty guineas, Dr. Graham offered couples young or old the means of begetting offspring. Patients were treated to a concert by four organs in unison, lasting a full hour. Streams of light played on "celestial pillows." In the morning the doctor checked the pulse of his patients, gave them breakfast, and sent the prospective parents home rejoicing.

Thomas Walker, an Englishman, discovered that bathing was the major cause of disease. He ceased washing altogether and said he felt much better.

Mary Baker Eddy inclined to this philosophy. She wrote in the 1875 edition of *Science and Health*, "The daily ablution of an infant is no more natural or necessary than to take a fish out of water and cover it with dirt once a day."

While Mrs. Eddy sold books claiming that all is spirit and there is no matter, Andrew Jackson Davis sold as many books proving that there is no spirit or mind, for all is matter and power.

Phineas Quimby of Maine healed with what he called "animal magnetism." He cured women patients by rubbing their heads with his right hand while placing his left on their bare abdomens. The animal magnetism flowed out of his body into theirs, he said.

The mentally ill were kept in cages like animals. They were beaten, bled, and drugged. In both London and Vienna, centers of science and culture, they were exhibited to the public like animals in a zoo.

Since isolated pioneers and farmers often took care of themselves the best they could, home health guides became popular. Dr. J. Boyd of Philadelphia published his *Family Medical Advisor* in 1845. He instructed parents to treat croup as follows:

"Let the little patient be bled very freely at the commencement of the case.

"Then give to the child of three years old or upwards a teaspoonful of antimonial wine (made by dissolving a scruple of emetic tartar in a pint of sherry wine), and repeat it, if necessary, in half an hour.

"If the second dose does not cause vomiting, double its quantity, unless the case be very mild. . . . The vomiting should be encouraged by warm drinks, and the nausea should be continued."

Another popular work called *The Family Medicine Chest Dispensatory* offered a standard assortment of medicines for $100. Remedies included prussic acid, "administered with advantage in consumption for allaying the cough;" asafoetida, "a medicine very serviceable in those hysterical affections to which delicate females are liable;" calomel as a cathartic, "children requiring larger doses in proportion than adults;" lunar caustic "employed internally in epilepsy and externally for lotions;" ipecacuanha to produce perspiration in colds, "no medicine more useful in the family than this;" laudanum "for procuring sleep;" and nux vomica "administered to excite the nervous system, especially in palsy." Tobacco was recommended as a remedy for affections of the lungs, "the vapor to be produced by smoking a cigar." The patient should frequently draw in the breath freely, so that the internal surface of the air vessels may be exposed to the action of the vapor."

But these were also years of inquiry, discovery, and reform. In 1846, Sir John Forbes, editor of the *British and Foreign Medical Review*, wrote an earnest editorial entitled "Young Physic" in which he called for natural remedies instead of the popular drugging of the day. In a concluding sum-

Pills, Potions, Purges, and Prussic Acid

A SICK CHILD IN THE FAMILY AND A COUNTRY DOCTOR WHO DID THE BEST HE COULD
—A FAMILIAR SCENE IN NINETEENTH-CENTURY AMERICA

Country doctor in the mountains of East Tennessee. Sketch by Healy in 1890.

BETTMANN ARCHIVE

Civil War Medicine: Dr. William A. Hammond combats overdrugging with calomel.

mary of his objectives, he wished "to endeavor to banish from the treatment of acute and dangerous diseases at least, the ancient axiom, 'melius anceps remedium quam nullam' [a doubtful remedy is better than none], and to substitute in its place the safer and wiser dogma that when we are not certain of an indication, we should give nature the best chance of doing the work herself, by leaving her operations undisturbed by those of art."

In 1858 Dr. Jacob Bigelow challenged the drugging philosophy in his *Exposition of Rational Medicine:* "Confinement by diseases, which might have terminated in a few days, was protracted to weeks and months because the importance of the case, as it was thought, required that the patient should be artificially 'taken down' and then artificially 'built up.' " "When carried to its 'heroic' extent, artificial medicine undermined the strength, elicited new morbid manifestations, and left more disease than it took away. The question raised was not how much the patient had profited under his active treatment, but how much more of the same he could bear."

Dr. Crawford Long, Charles Jackson, and William Morton experimented with ether anesthesia, and Boston's Oliver Wendell Holmes wrote on "The Contagiousness of Puerperal Fever." In 1860 Dr. Holmes called for an end of "drugging," the "heroic" method. Except for opium and wine, which were useful for pain, he said that the "whole materia medica, as now used, could be

Wayside diagnosis, after a painting, 1889.

The Vision Bold

sunk to the bottom of the sea."

The French artist Honore Daumier depicted a nineteenth-century physician and his high fatality rate pondering, "Why the devil does it happen that all my patients succumb?—I bleed them well, purge them, drug them.... I simply can't understand."

However, health standards among most Americans remained primitive. Schools offered no health education; no government health programs existed. Little was known of nutrition. The concept of sanitation had scarcely been dreamed of. Before Pasteur, germs had not been discovered. People thought fresh air, especially night air, was injurious. They shunned sunshine and considered bathing in winter as hazardous at best. Women wore tightly laced corsets. Most frontier folk subsisted on salt pork, black coffee, and corn bread kneaded with vast amounts of lard.

A young man who heeded Horace Greeley's advice to "Go west, young man, go west" did so and wrote, "Indigestion is all the fashion of the great West." It is said that the words "How are you?" were less a greeting than a serious inquiry!

As might be expected, John and Ann Kellogg responded warmly to the concept of "rational" medicine. They had also become interested in other Adventist beliefs and were a part of the movement. Funds from the sale of their farm helped to provide steam printing presses that would publish, among other things, a journal on health—*The Health Reformer*. With their large family, they resided in Battle Creek where they operated a broom factory.

Though neither family could have foreseen it then, the names Kellogg and White would in the years ahead figure prominently in the development of health knowledge, major health institutions, and a saner, more rational practice of the healing arts.

With extravagant claims and guarantees, Sears, Roebuck and Company offered patented remedies and "cures."

30

Pills, Potions, Purges, and Prussic Acid

Purging for many was a way of life. Dr Guy Patin, French physician and a leader of the Paris faculty, points with pride to proven success obtained from his favorite cathartic prescription.

The Vision Bold

"The Druggist's Assistant." Drugging had its critics, as is shown in this cartoon. The skeleton points to a jar labeled "poison." In the glass case under the druggist's hand are containers of "Drop-Dead-Drops."

Pills, Potions, Purges, and Prussic Acid

Homeopath: "If you take me, you'll die of the disease." Allopath: "If you take me, you'll die of the cure." Patient: "It's all the same to me."

Tired of swallowing poison and useless nostrums, reformers declared war on druggists and drugging.

A little dubious, but determined, a mother gets ready for her youngster a dose of medicine for what ails him.

The Vision Bold

WEIRD AND WONDERFUL IDEAS ABOUNDED IN THE NINETEENTH-CENTURY WORLD OF MEDICINE, BUT "HEALTH REFORM" GRADUALLY DISPELLED SOME OF THE WORST OF THEM

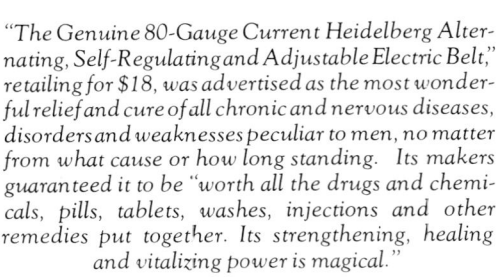

Phrenologists judged character and mentality on the basis of skull conformation. Dr. John H. Kellogg said these men "have set themselves up as phrenologists, head-examiners, bump-feelers, — blunderers would be a much more proper term to attach to them, — when in fact they hardly possessed intelligence and mother-wit enough to become first-class barbers. The amount of trash which has been retailed about the country, especially in the rural districts, under the name of phrenology is appalling. The harm that these charlatans do is incalculable."

"The Genuine 80-Gauge Current Heidelberg Alternating, Self-Regulating and Adjustable Electric Belt," retailing for $18, was advertised as the most wonderful relief and cure of all chronic and nervous diseases, disorders and weaknesses peculiar to men, no matter from what cause or how long standing. Its makers guaranteed it to be "worth all the drugs and chemicals, pills, tablets, washes, injections and other remedies put together. Its strengthening, healing and vitalizing power is magical."

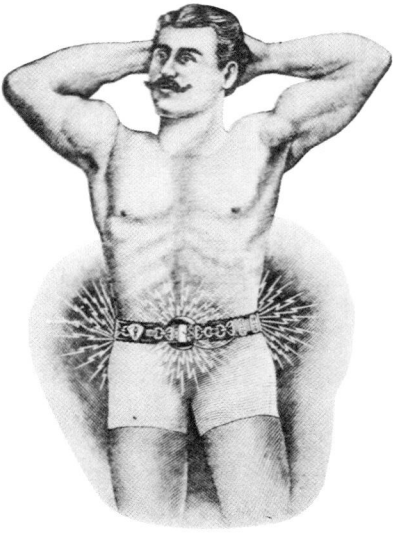

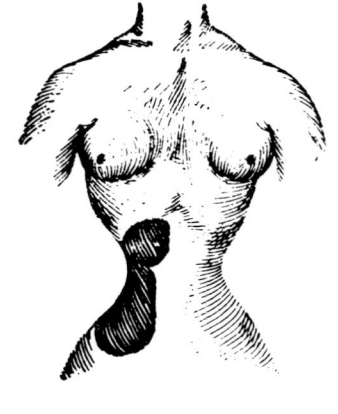

Health educators aimed some of their strongest ammunition at corset wearing. Dr. Kellogg wrote: "We scarcely ever met a lady who would admit that her corset was tight, and we have had occasion to speak with hundreds of ladies on this point in making medical examinations. We read the other day in a newspaper of a young woman who actually broke a rib in the attempt to gain another half-inch on her corset string. She well deserved the accident, no doubt; but the chances are ten to one that she would assert . . . that her corset was 'quite loose,' and to demonstrate the matter would show you how much more she could pinch up when she tried."

Pills, Potions, Purges, and Prussic Acid

Some people are using hydrotherapy more, and enjoying it less. In the early days of water cures, practitioners often did as much damage as the druggers, blisterers, and bleeders with indiscriminate use of very cold water, or very hot, regardless of patients' diseases or circumstances. Of Priessnitz, an Austrian water-cure pioneer, Kellogg wrote that "his lamentable want of knowledge allowed him to fall into many errors," but "he became more careful and discriminating in later years."—Illustration from *Good Health* magazine.

"The Improved Rational Body Brace is an abdominal supporter and shoulder brace combined, constructed so as to form a natural support of every organ of the body, including the spine, ribs, lungs, heart, liver, bowels, womb; in fact every organ, bone and muscle of the human body. . . . The healing influence of the Brace has never been approached by any other appliance."

"Princess Hair Restorer Grooms Hair Like This. The only absolutely effective, unfailingly successful, perfectly harmless, positively no-dye preparation on the market. If you do not find it all and more than we claim for it, . . . stopping hair from falling out, restoring natural color, curing dandruff or promoting a new growth of hair on a bald head, return it to us at once and we will cheerfully refund your money."

WILL SUCCESS SPOIL JOHN KELLOGG?

A Fledgling Health Institute Turns Up a Many-sided Genius

Profoundly disappointed and discouraged persons usually make poor material out of which to construct a church. And it would have been hard to find a more dejected group than the thousands of Millerites who had so confidently expected the return of Jesus in the fall of 1844. That dramatic event, they felt sure, would be the beginning of a new life, satisfying beyond their fondest dreams. But it didn't happen that way, and even the messages of encouragement and love communicated to them through a young woman did not help them sort things out in their minds very fast.

Seventeen-year-old Ellen Harmon of Portland, Maine, was known to the Advent believers for her devout life. Still, few of them at first accepted the idea that God would give "Sister Ellen" supernatural visions full of encouragement, instruction, and reproof. It took nearly twenty years before twenty-one delegates, representing 3,500 believers, who among other things had come to accept Ellen Harmon's prophetic call, formally constituted the Seventh-day Adventist Church. In the years preceding that May 21, 1863 gathering, Ellen and the energetic Adventist preacher, James White, who had been her husband since 1846, traveled thousands of miles, held scores of meetings, and wrote hundreds of pages in their efforts to salvage a remnant from the thousands of advent believers whom William Miller had aroused in the preceding two decades.

All this activity, coupled with keeping house, raising a family, and a great deal of earnest Bible study, had not left much time for Ellen White to concern herself with principles of healthful living. In 1848 she had begun to teach that her fellow Adventists should discard tobacco, tea, and coffee. But she left health matters mostly to doctors and the temperance lectures who, since the 1830's, had been promoting a variety of curious concoctions to cure America's aches and pains. Her attitude changed dramatically as the result of a vision given her in a farm living room near Otsego, Michigan, on June 6, 1863. There, as she and James joined in evening prayers with the Hilliard family, Ellen received a forty-five minute vision in which certain principles of healthful living were presented to her.

Ellen was shown that Christians had a "sacred duty" to attend to their health and to "arouse others" to this duty. She was shown that true temperance involves far more than alcoholic beverages; it applies to work, to foods, to the use of drugs. True remedies for illness are "natural" ones: water, proper diet, fresh air, exercise, rest, and sunshine.

Never one to shirk a responsibility, Ellen White immediately began to teach the principles of healthful living on her next speaking tour through New York and New England. At the close of an address, hearers frequently asked her if she had read the publications of Drs. Russell Trall and James Caleb Jackson, many of whose ideas resembled hers. "No," Ellen would reply, she had not read Trall's or Jackson's works, nor did she intend to until she had written out what the Lord had shown her.

His curiosity aroused, James White began to collect books, pamphlets, and journals on health

Dr. James Caleb Jackson established Our Home on the Hillside, the famous water-cure spa at Dansville, New York, to which James White was taken after a stroke disabled him in 1865. Dr. Jackson recommended less prayer and religious exercise for Elder White, but Ellen White did not agree, and eventually took her husband away.

Dr. Russell T. Trall founded the Hygieo-Therapeutic College in New Jersey, where he offered a twenty-week medical course. Both Merritt Kellogg and John H. Kellogg studied medicine there; but John wanted better training than the opinionated health reformer offered, so he continued studies in Michigan and New York.

written by Trall, Jackson, and other early nineteenth-century health reformers like Sylvester Graham and Dr. L. B. Coles. Once Ellen had completed her initial series of articles on health and hygiene, she began to read these earlier works and "was surprised to find them so nearly in harmony" with what the Lord had shown her. She and James decided they could safely recommend such works to the infant Adventist Church, now struggling to understand just what changes in health habits God wanted them to adopt.

Perhaps without realizing who Jackson was and what he taught, the Whites had had occasion to follow his advice a few months before Ellen's Otsego vision. In the midst of a January, 1863, diphtheria epidemic, two of the White children came down with the disease. Coincidentally, a friend called James White's attention to a letter published in a local paper in which Dr. Jackson outlined a successful treatment for diphtheria, based on water treatments, ventilation of the sickroom, rest, and careful home nursing. Impressed with this article, the Whites followed the treatment. Both children recovered, and Ellen experienced similar success when she again followed this program with a sick six-year-old neighbor boy. Elder White decided that Jackson's letter was so valuable that he reprinted it in the *Advent Review and Sabbath Herald*, the general church paper he edited.

THE WATER-CURE JOURNAL.

AND HERALD OF REFORMS, DEVOTED TO
Physiology, Hydropathy, and the Laws of Life.

VOL. XII. NO. 5.]   NEW YORK, NOVEMBER, 1851.   [$1.00 A YEAR.

FOWLERS & WELLS, PUBLISHERS,
131 Nassau street, New York.

Contents.

The Medical Profession, . . . 97	American Hydropathic Institute, ... 114
Teething and its Management, 101	A Puff for the "Regular" Profession, . . 114
Chemistry of Life, No. III., 103	A Good Dentist, . . . 115
Children's Dress, . . . 104	The class of the A. H. Institute, 115
Woman's Dress, . . . 105	Female Medical Colleges, . 115
Effects of Coffee and Tea on Human Health, . . . 106	Lectures on the Water-Cure, 115
Is Water Treatment Applicable in City Practice, . . 108	A Good Example, . . . 115
Bilious Fever — Home Treatment, ... 108	Unwholesome Fruit — Beware of Grapes, . . . 116
November Topics, . . . 109	Good News, ... 116
Hydropathy and Homœopathy, 109	The Yellow Springs Water-Cure, ... 116
Animal Excretions as Medicines, ... 109	Business Notices, . . . 116
Expanding the Chest, . . 109	Presents, ... 116
Biographical Sketch of Sylvester Graham, . . . 110	To Teachers and Writers, . 116
The Hunger Cure, . . . 111	The Right and Proper Way, 116
The Cure of Fever and Ague, 111	Varieties, ... 116
Home Cases of Water-Cure in Childbirth, . . . 112	Diary of a Honeymoon, . 116
Home Treatment in Michigan, 112	The Curse League, . . 117
Reviews, ... 112	Hard Times, ... 117
The Water Cure in America, 113	To Correspondents, . . 119
Miscellany, ... 113	Book Notices, . . . 118
Gossips from Boston, . . 113	Advertisements, . . . 119
Drippings from a Wet Sheet, No. II. 114	Water-Cure Establishments, 119

The Causes of Disease.—The first cause of disease is hereditary transmission or predisposition. A child may be born actually diseased, as with syphilis, scrofula, salt-rheum, tubercles in the lungs, etc., derived from the father or mother, or with such a weakened vitality that it cannot resist the common diseasing influences. A diseased father can not beget, a diseased mother can not bring forth, a healthy child. A child, the very germ of whose existence is depraved, who partakes, for the nine months of its fœtal life, of the weakness, pain, and suffering of a sick mother, whose very life-blood is made of bad food and impure air, narcotics and medicinal poisons, and who continues to live for some months longer on the same unhealthy nutriment, drawn from her breast, has a poor chance for life, and none at all for a healthy existence.

Vanity.—To become a regular contributor to a magazine or newspaper, and afterwards make frequent allusions to the great improvement visible in its columns.

THE MEDICAL PROFESSION.

AN INAUGURAL ADDRESS, GIVEN AT THE OPENING OF THE AMERICAN HYDROPATHIC INSTITUTE, NEW YORK, SEPTEMBER 15, 1851.

BY T. L. NICHOLS, M. D.

The American Hydropathic Institute is the first Medical School established for the purpose of teaching the principles and practice of Hydropathy, or the Water-Cure.

The greatest of human enterprises have small beginnings, and from this law of development and progress our institution claims no exemption. Vast forests spring from microscopic germs. Behemoth and Leviathan could once swim in a single drop of water. The overshadowing power of Eternal Rome began with the gathering of a little band of fugitives and marauders. America, which now grasps two oceans, and bids fair to control the destinies of the world, began her wonderful career within a few forlorn and scattering settlements.

Moral revolutions have been subject to the same law. The Star in the East lighted the first Christian shrine in a stable at Bethlehem. Mahomet, whose doctrines now govern half the human race, for years had his wife as his only disciple.

We are not to despise the day of small things; nor must we reject the truth because it is not yet sustained by majorities, supported by authorities, nor sanctioned by antiquity. We must not forget that the gravest errors of the world have all this sustenance, support, and sanction. Every newly-discovered truth stands, at first, in a minority of one, with age, authority, and the power of numbers arrayed against it. If all men were conservative, the world could make no progress. If it would be stereotyped with all its errors. If all men believed in the wisdom of majorities, no new truth could ever find disciples. If all men were enslaved by authorities, farewell to the hopes of a happier future. We must not forget that every reformer who has aided in the enlightenment and elevation of the human race must have stood alone, at first, with the whole world of custom, habit, fashion, science, authority, and antiquity — the accumulated wisdom of ages — arrayed against him.

Misdirected reverence is the bane of philosophy. Men should reverence God, Nature, Truth, and Eternal Justice. Men should not reverence a benighted antiquity, reveries, misnamed science, the accumulated errors of ages, and the institutions of despotism. A man should look back upon the wrongs, falsehoods, and darkness of antiquity as he looks upon the follies and obliquities of his own infancy and childhood. They are not to be reverenced nor repeated. The past has its lessons; but it teaches us, for the most part, what to avoid. The true man must look to the present as his field of work, and to the future for his visions of glory. Humanity is struggling with the swaddling clothes of its infancy. These clothes of infancy are the fetters of youth, which our conservative philosophers are intent on making us wear forever. The experience of the last century has taught mankind some useful lessons. One by one the cherished errors of ages, in science, philosophy, and government, have been exploded. The Old has fought against the New; the Old, entrenched in its fortresses of custom, upheld by reverence for antiquity, and supported by majorities; but truth is mighty, and the simple power of its enunciation causes the strongholds of error to crumble, as the walls of Jericho fell before the blasts of Hebrew trumpets.

The lesson of recent experience in science and philosophy is this:—Respect no doctrine on account of its age, the learned authorities by which it is supported, or the multitudes which believe in it. Reject no doctrine because it is new—because its teachers have their fame yet to acquire—and because it is as yet unsupported by the prestige of numbers. Practice the precept of the Apostle—a precept of mingled radicalism and conservatism—"Prove *all* things; hold fast to that which is *good*." The most radical can ask no more than that we should examine, try, test, or "prove all things;" the most conservative must be content, if we "hold fast to that which is good." This is the divinely inspired maxim of human progress; now beginning to be understood, reverenced, and obeyed.

In applying these principles to the medical profession, I shall speak of it as it *has been* and *is* ; and as it *should be*. It is recognized as one of the three learned professions, and as among the most im-

The lobby of Our Home on the Hillside, Dr. Jackson's famed spa.

OUR HOME ON THE HILLSIDE Dansville, New York

At Dr. Jackson's Our Home on the Hillside visitors enjoyed excellent air, water, and scenery, besides receiving "hydropathic" treatments given with moderation and good sense. However, some of Jackson's views were extreme. He banned table salt completely, and boasted, "In my entire practice I have never given a dose of medicine; not so much as I should have administered had I taken a homeopathic pellet of the seven-millionth dilution, and dissolving it in Lake Superior, given my friends of its waters." Various prominent Adventists, including Elder and Mrs. John N. Andrews, were appreciative guests of Our Home, and Drs. Horatio S. Lay and Phebe Lamson served here before the opening of the Western Health Reform Institute in Battle Creek.

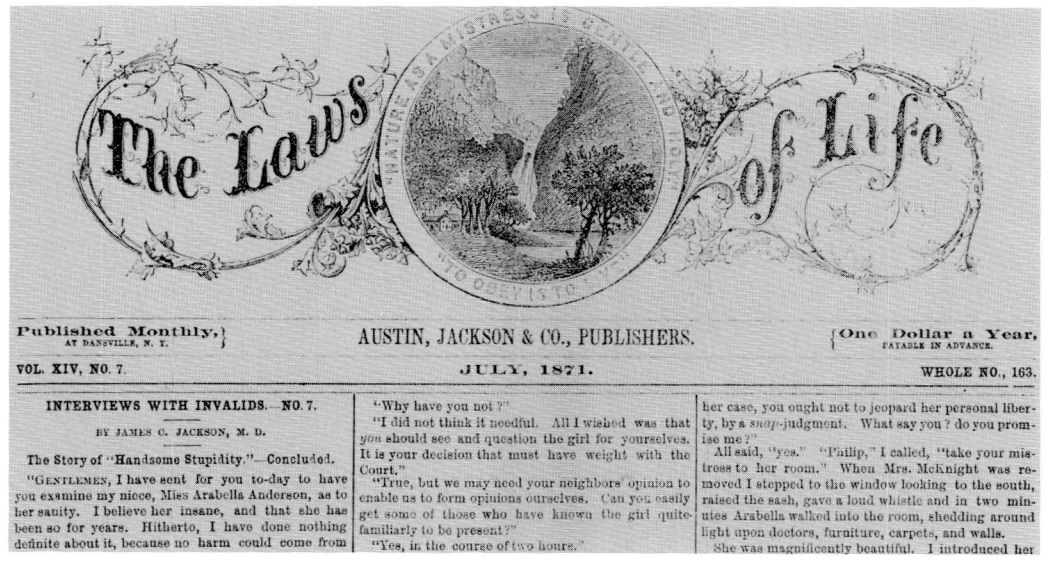

The Laws of Life, *Dr. Jackson's famed health journal.*

Almost a year later, another experience that touched their immediate family confirmed the Whites' faith in simple natural remedies. Their eldest son, Henry, died from pneumonia in spite of conventional treatment by the family physician. Several weeks later, ten-year-old Willie, Ellen's third son, developed the same malady. After much prayer, the troubled parents decided to fight for this boy's life with simple water treatments. An anxious week followed; but the crisis passed, and Willie quickly regained his health.

With this background, it was natural for the Whites to decide to visit Our Home on the Hillside, the health institution Dr. Jackson operated at Dansville, in New York's picturesque Finger Lakes District. Jackson had begun his career as a temperance and antislavery lecturer. During a bout with ill health in 1849, he had been treated at a small water cure in western New York. Here he embraced hydropathic methods then in vogue in reform circles. After taking one of the rapid medical courses available, Dr. Jackson then helped operate the Glen Haven Water Cure. Several years later he acquired a bankrupt, decrepit water cure at Dansville. Its principal advantages were a magnificent view of the Genesee Valley and a liberal supply of fresh water from an "all-healing spring" which had reputedly burst forth from the mountainside one morning some sixty years earlier. On these slender assets Jackson built a famous health resort which served at least 300 guests at the time the Whites arrived from their home in Battle Creek in 1864.

Some weeks before the Whites' visit, an Adventist physician from Allegan, Michigan, Dr. Horatio S. Lay, had journeyed with his invalid wife to test the curative powers of the Jackson program. He was persuaded to join the medical staff at "Our Home," and now served as interpreter of the Dansville system to the Whites. James and Ellen found much to commend at Jackson's institution. The scenery was delightful; the air and water fresh and pure. The Whites had already made numerous changes in their dietary habits, so they did not find the absence of butter, salt, meat, or greasy foods disturbing. Both felt that there was an actual danger of eating too liberally of the generous assortment of vegetables, fruits, and grain products provided.

James and Ellen had been a little fearful of the type of water treatments they might find at Our Home. Many water cures used the "heroic treatment," which required patients to drink up to forty glasses of water daily and placed heavy reliance on frequent ice-cold baths. They were happily surprised at the moderate and rational variety of baths Jackson used, and the sensible amounts of water his patients were asked to drink. But not everything at "Our Home" pleased the Adventist visitors. In Ellen's estimation, Dr. Jackson placed too much emphasis on recreation of the wrong type. The weekly dance, the amateur theatrical productions, and the constant card playing she "could not countenance." Although she admitted that these amusements might serve some useful purpose for non-Christians, she was equally sure that these would injure the religious experience of church members. On balance, however, Ellen believed there should be a similar institution in Michigan to which ill Sabbath-keeping Adventists could resort.

After a three-week visit at Dansville, the Whites resumed a demanding schedule of traveling, speaking, and writing. Within the next few months, they prepared a series of 64- to 80-page pamphlets devoted to six aspects of healthful living: diet, water treatments, the misuse of drugs, proper clothing, fresh air, and exercise. Ellen wrote a major article for each pamphlet, while James selected pertinent materials from the writings of Jackson, Trall, Graham, Coles, and others to fill out the remainder of each number. In addition to these editorial duties, Elder White was heavily involved in complications that arose because Seventh-day Adventists took a noncombatant position in the War Between the States. By late 1864, the draft was affecting many Adventist young men, and Elder White assumed a major role in raising funds to provide $300 exemption payments for them. Thus a man could discharge his obligation to his country without violating his conscience.

In the spring of 1865, James White was elected president of the Adventist General Conference for his first term. This increased his already heavy traveling commitments. Difficult railway schedules kept him from getting needed sleep, and added administrative responsibilities sapped his vital forces. The strain proved too much, and on the morning of August 16, 1865, while walking with Ellen in a neighbor's garden near their Battle Creek home, he suffered a paralytic stroke. Earnest prayer followed, and his condition improved somewhat. Yet soon he appeared to hit a plateau, and local doctors declared that only a miracle would restore him.

For five weeks, Ellen nursed her invalid husband with utmost care and devotion, but he improved no further. At last she decided to take him to Our Home on the Hillside for consultation and treatment. Dr. Lay came out to accompany the Whites and two other ailing Adventist leaders, Elders J. N. Loughborough and Uriah Smith, to Dansville. Dr. Jackson received the little group with great courtesy and held out hope for James White's complete recovery, but only after six to eight months of complete rest and treatment.

Faithfully, the Whites visited the treatment rooms five times a week for prescribed baths. They strolled on the scenic paths around the institution's grounds. They followed the suggested diet. Yet James did not seem to improve, and Ellen noticed that Dr. Jackson's complete ban on salt affected her digestion adversely. Searching for the reasons behind the failure of Elder White to respond to treatment, Dr. Jackson decided that the prayer services held three times a day in the White quarters were partially to blame. The stroke had been brought on, the doctor thought, because of Elder White's excessive preoccupation with religious matters. It would be necessary to relax religious exercises and divert James with carefree amusements. Ellen objected violently; this would be a denial of faith. She was also convinced that her husband already suffered from too much inactivity. His mind and body, she felt, needed a different type of challenge, one more demanding than bed rest and mild walks.

After three months, Ellen decided to move James to the home of friends in Rochester, New York, some forty-five miles away. Several leading Adventist ministers came to pray with the Whites and encourage them. As Christmas Day, 1865, drew to a close, a small group joined James and Ellen for earnest prayer, during which Ellen was given a second vision emphasizing the importance of healthful living. She saw that Adventist believers generally had been too lax in changing their diet, and embracing views of hygiene and treatment of illness to which she had been directed eighteen months earlier. The health teachings, she saw, were to be as integrally connected with the Adventist religious witness "as the arm and hand with the human body." She saw dangers in relying on popular health institutions of the day, and was directed that Adventists should have an institution to care for their own sick and to provide a place where many might "learn how to take care of their bodies that they may prevent sickness."

Although James was not miraculously healed, his wife decided that they should return to Battle

James White. *Health problems led him to seek relief at Dr. Jackson's institution. Later he persuaded J. H. Kellogg to leave teaching and study medicine.*

John N. Loughborough. *He solicited the first funds for the Western Health Reform Institute, and served as first president, board of trustees.*

John N. Andrews. *He joined Loughborough in raising money for the new health institution, securing pledges for $800 in Olcott, New York.*

Uriah Smith. *Long-time editor of the* Review and Herald, *he urged believers to buy stock in the institute, and was secretary of the board of trustees.*

The Western Health Reform Institute opened in September, 1866, with a ten-bed capacity and one patient. Its most outstanding piece of equipment was a windmill-operated pump which supplied copious amounts of water for baths and treatments.

Creek. That winter, despite the advice of friends, she began to take him out to visit small companies of Advent believers in central Michigan. Sometimes they traveled for hours by sleigh across the crisp snows. These outings had no adverse affect on Elder White; in fact, he seemed slowly to improve.

In the spring of 1866, the General Conference again met in Battle Creek in annual session. To this group, Ellen White addressed a stirring appeal. No longer must there be delay on the part of ministers or laymen in putting the principles of healthful living into practice. And Seventh-day Adventists *must* have a health institution of their own. The delegates, strongly moved, voted to accept health reform. They later decided to launch a health journal to present proper principles to Adventist and non-Adventist alike.

The job of editing the new monthly journal, christened the *Health Reformer*, was assigned to Dr. H. S. Lay, now back in Michigan. The first issue came out the following August. Since there were few Adventist physicians at the time, much of the material was written by preachers. Ellen White contributed an article on the duty of each person to understand his body, how it functioned, and how to keep it in health. She concluded by saying that "ignorance upon this important subject is sin."

There was going to be a Seventh-day Adventist health institution, too, although church leaders were less certain as to just how this might be brought about. James White, Adventism's most efficient fund raiser, was still much too ill to assume responsibility for such a project. Finally, with considerable misgivings, Elder J. N. Loughborough, president of the local Michigan Conference of Adventists, drew up a subscription list and set out to see what he could do to round up the necessary money. He decided first to call on John Preston Kellogg, Battle Creek grocer and broommaker who had moved from New England to Flint, Michigan, and later to Battle Creek. It was a strategic choice, as Kellogg had proved to be a liberal supporter of the church in times past. He had been one of three to supply funds to move the denominational press from Rochester, New York, to Battle Creek and a major supporter of early tent evangelism in Michigan.

After Loughborough had finished with his appeal, Kellogg reached for the subscription list. In a bold hand he placed his name at the top, along with the figure $500. "That much is a seed to start the institution," he told Loughborough, "and I'll venture it, sink or swim." The ball was rolling. Ellen White also pledged $500; other members of the church in Battle Creek raised the total to $1825. Over in Olcott, New York, Elder J. N. Andrews persuaded the local believers to pledge an additional $800. They made further appeals through columns of the church paper and through letters to each congregation. By August, 1866, the response was so encouraging that the leaders could announce plans to open a health reform institute in Battle Creek the following month. Here Seventh-day Adventists might come as "hygienic boarders" to learn how to better care for their bodies, to overcome wrong habits, and to be fitted for translation. Here non-Adventists could be helped physically and, in pleasant surroundings, be given a correct view of the Adventist faith.

Apparently no one even considered locating the Western Health Reform Institute, as the new project was named, any place but in Battle Creek. Although still a city of fewer than 5,000, Battle Creek had become the acknowledged center of Seventh-day Adventist activities. Thus it was logical for the Institute developers to look for a site in the city's West End, where most Adventists lived. They discovered that the two-story residence of Judge Benjamin F. Graves, which included a small cottage and five acres of land, was available. The project moved along quickly. They speedily remodeled Graves's eight-room house and built an addition for the hydrotherapy department. They also secured two more acres of land and a second cottage. As promised, the Institute opened to receive patients early in September, 1866.

Both Dr. Lay and Dr. Phebe Lamson, who constituted the entire medical staff on opening day, had served as staff members at Jackson's Our Home on the Hillside. Two bath attendants, an untrained nurse, and several general purpose "helpers" assisted them at the outset. The institute's ten-bed capacity was not strained on opening day; only one patient arrived! That situation changed quickly, however; within two months Dr. Lay could report that patients at the institute had arrived from nine different states ranging from Rhode Island to Iowa, and also from Canada. They hired additional rooms outside the regular buildings for the use of ambulatory patients.

One may be permitted a smile of amusement at enthusiastic early descriptions of the institute's facilities, which laid heavy stress on the eight-foot windmill, capable if the breeze was right of filling a barrel of water in three to five minutes and pumping it up to the 300-barrel tank poised above the bath room. From here, gravity carried the water either to a fifty-barrel heating tank on the ground floor, or direct to the bathers. This massive water heater made it possible to provide patients with exactly the temperature of bath prescribed. A contemplation of modern hospital charges can also make one nostalgic for the good old days when "Health Reform Institute" charges ran from $5 to $7 per *week*, including room, board, treatments, and nursing and medical care!

The institute operated for eight months before it was incorporated. The only state law under which the institute could legally organize was intended for profit-making manufacturing and mining corporations. Finally, in March, 1867, the Michigan legislature amended this law to allow for the establishment of health institutions, but still as profit-bearing stock corporations. Finally, on April 9, 1867, ten persons, holding collectively 70 shares of $25 par stock, signed the articles of incorporation. These men included John Preston

Horatio S. Lay, M.D., and Phebe Lamson, M.D., were the physicians in charge when the institute opened. Dr. Kate Lindsay, at right, later joined them in the endeavor.

Kellogg, Dr. Horatio S. Lay, and two prominent Adventist preachers, J. N. Loughborough and Uriah Smith. The latter two became president and secretary, respectively, of the board of trustees. The institute's founders obviously intended it to be an exclusively denominational enterprise. They advertised stock for sale to "any person keeping the commandments of God and the faith of Jesus Christ." If that language still wasn't clear, provisions for voting prescribed that proxies must be certified "by the elder or clerk of the Seventh-day Adventist church to which such person belongs" or by any Adventist minister in good standing.

The acceptance accorded the Western Health Reform Institute was gratifying to its director, Dr. Lay. Within four months' time he called for construction of a large building costing perhaps $25,000. To him the need was obvious; with his present facilities crowded, he feared to advertise widely lest more patients arrive than could be accommodated. Elders Loughborough and Smith picked up the refrain and called the faithful to purchase shares of stock. The board of directors showed how profitable the enterprise could be when, as one of their first official acts, they declared an initial 10 percent dividend. This turned out to be not only the first but also the last such dividend.

Ellen White was not pleased with the course of events. She saw the lure of expected profits drawing the limited funds of the small coterie of Adventist believers away from nonprofit branches of the church's work. Largely because of the Whites' counsel, the second annual stockholders meeting did a radical about-face. They voted to place future institutional profits at the disposal of the directors to be used for charitable purposes. Should current investors find this arrangement unsatisfactory, provision was made to purchase their stock as soon as the corporation could do so.

The institute management's expansive building plans also troubled the Whites. Ellen favored slow, steady growth rather than mushrooming facilities. Dozens of hygienic institutions had been started in the previous twenty-five years, she noted, but few of those which had stayed with the original principles remained. She also feared that a Dansville-type emphasis on questionable recreation would follow too-rapid growth. Although management had already laid foundations for the proposed new building, work now stopped and construction materials already purchased were sold.

John Kellogg attended Dr. Trall's Hygieo-Therapeutic College, the University of Michigan, and finally Bellevue Hospital Medical College.

A sudden downturn in the institute's finances proved the wisdom of the Whites' counsel to go slow. The directors had decided to use institute profits to provide lower rates for needy church members. This resulted in a deluge of poverty-stricken patients, and Dr. Lay seemed unable to prevent these charity patients from staying on and on. Family problems also kept him from devoting himself fully to his patients; he became irritable and impatient with them. Profits disappeared, and three years after it had opened the institute was $13,000 in debt. Only eight patients were paying full prices. Reorganization of the management seemed essential. James White, fully recovered, was elected president of the board of directors. He brought several Adventist businessmen, including J. P. Kellogg, who became the institute's treasurer, onto the board. Dr. Lay returned to private practice in Allegan.

Although James White's firm hand arrested the institute's decline, he knew he could not for long let this branch of the Adventist cause preoccupy his time. His interests were too broad; they encompassed writing, publishing, education, evangelism, and organization. A well-trained physician was needed, a man gifted with energy and managerial ability and at the same time grounded in the health principles Ellen White had been shown. As the Whites cast about for such a man, their attention centered more and more on J. P. Kellogg's son John Harvey, just then completing his teen-age years.

John Harvey Kellogg was no stranger to the Whites. While young John was still a lad, James White had persuaded the elder Kellogg to allow the boy to learn the printing trade in the Adventist publishing house. John had moved up the ladder from printer's devil to typesetter and proofreader. He helped set the type for Ellen White's first articles on healthful living and found the principles propounded persuasively attractive. Later the youthful Kellogg read widely in the works of earlier American health reformers. He became a zealous convert, and this zeal the Whites had observed firsthand. The summer before the institute's reorganization, John Harvey stayed at the White farm near Greenville, Michigan, where Elder White was completing recovery from his long illness by engaging in outdoor activities. John aided in the farm chores and also helped Elder White in editorial work and sermon copying. James saw in this young man the drive and energy, the genius for organization, the nimble and inquiring mind which a man desires in a son.

There was one problem. John Harvey Kellogg had decided to be a schoolteacher. Having taught one year in a country school, he matriculated in the teacher-training course at Michigan State Normal College in Ypsilanti. The Whites decided to enlist family support in getting young John to change his plans. Working through his older half-brother Merritt, a graduate of Dr. Russell Trall's six-month medical course, the Whites persuaded John to join their own two sons and another young Adventist in accompanying Merritt to Trall's Hygieo-Therapeutic College. While the older brother gained more experience through repeating the medical course, the younger Kellogg could get a deeper knowledge of health and medical matters. He could still be a teacher—a teacher of one of the most important of all subjects, the way to good health.

Although Trall's medical school was in decline by the time John Kellogg studied there, its intellectual stimulus still proved great enough to capture the young man's interest. From the start, he was the most diligent of twenty students in at-

By the time Kellogg became chief physician in 1876, the institute had grown to 100 beds, with eight buildings on fifteen acres. James White quipped, "Our buildings are already larger than our doctors."

tendance, often staying up until two or three in the morning to study. John readily accepted the emphasis Trall placed on hydrotherapy, correct diet, exercise, fresh air, and sunshine, but he strongly disagreed when the opinionated Trall scathingly attacked the idea that there was any such thing as "organic" chemistry. John's reading had led him to believe otherwise. Although granted an M.D. by Trall's school at the close of a twenty-week course, John Kellogg did not even consider going into practice. But his appetite for medical knowledge had been aroused. He must get the best available.

Elder White had probably expected just such a development. With his blessing and a loan of $1,000, John Harvey left Battle Creek to further his medical education. First he spent a year studying at the University of Michigan Medical School, then in 1875 completed a regular M.D. at Bellevue Hospital Medical College in New York City. At that time, Bellevue was recognized as the nation's leading medical school, having pioneered the concept of combining clinical observation with lectures. Its location in America's largest metropolis afforded students an unparalleled opportunity to observe a variety of ailments. Kellogg demonstrated his eagerness for thorough preparation by taking private instruction beyond the required classes from Drs. Austin Flint, Sr., and Edward G. Janeway, two of Bellevue's most able diagnosticians. While still at Bellevue, Kellogg also began editing *The Health Reformer*. That journal had gone into decline when Dr. Lay left Battle Creek. Finally, James White had taken over and begun the job of rejuvenating the *Reformer*. John Kellogg had actually been doing much of the editorial work for Elder White before officially becoming editor.

Meanwhile, the fortunes of the Western Health Reform Institute gradually improved under the leadership of James White and several doctors, none of whom stayed long. By 1871, the institute consisted of eight buildings and spread itself over 15 acres of land. The facilities accommodated 100 patients. Two years later James White reported that of the 70 patients then at the institute "not 1/5" were Seventh-day Adventists. This in spite of the fact that advertising appeared only in Adventist publications. These developments led some church leaders again to suggest construction of a large main building. But in mid-1874 Elder White still demurred. "Our institute buildings are already larger than our doctors," he said.

Shortly after John Kellogg's return to Battle Creek from Bellevue, the staff accepted the young doctor as a member. Several months later, James White, who had become disenchanted with Dr. William Russell, the institute's chief physician, persuaded the directors to offer Russell's job to Kellogg. Although John believed he could improve things at the institute, he was cognizant of his twenty-three years and youthful looks, and determined to spend his life in research and writing. Thus he refused the position. Quite probably he was also influenced by Ellen White's opinion that the time for him to lead the institute had not yet come.

Knowing that the directors lacked confidence in him, Dr. Russell found it difficult to provide effective leadership. Soon the institute's fortunes were once more in decline. In the summer of 1876, with Ellen White's encouragement, the directors renewed their invitation to Dr. Kellogg to become chief physician, threatening to close the institute if he did not accept. They compromised. Kellogg agreed to take over for one year, beginning October 1, 1876. That year stretched into sixty-seven, as he was still medical director at the time of his death in 1943.

What was to become a whole new era began inauspiciously. Only twenty patients remained at the institute on October 1, 1876, and six of them left with Dr. Russell when he opened a rival water cure in Ann Arbor. Two more took one

Battle Creek Sanitarium bath girls about 1890.

look at the five-foot-four stripling physician and decided to depart. That left twelve.

If Kellogg was disheartened, he determined not to show it. With the backing of James White, he threw himself into a whirlwind of activities designed to improve the institute's image. Deciding that a name change would help, and without waiting for the directors' approval, he rechristened the institution Battle Creek Sanitarium. The term *sanatorium* was already widely used to indicate a special hospital for treatment of diseases such as tuberculosis. Kellogg claimed that the variation of the word he devised meant a place where people learned to stay well. John Harvey was not the first to coin the word. *Sanitarium* appears in the English press as far back as 1851, the year before he was born. Kellogg did, however, popularize the term in the United States.

Better doctor-patient relationships became an immediate Kellogg objective. He personally examined each incoming patient and continued to see them at regular intervals. He had the rare ability of communicating to every patient the impression that his or her case was the most important concern of the Sanitarium. He quickly developed a devoted following. Detractors complained that he had a particular gift for cultivating the wealthy. This was undoubtedly true, but he also spent long hours with, and exhibited genuine concern for, humble workingmen and women as well.

Recognizing the value of good community relations, Dr. Kellogg made it a point to invite Battle Creek residents to the programs and concerts presented for Sanitarium patients. He also cultivated the regular medical profession. This was in contrast to the tendency of most reform physicians like Dr. Trall, who belabored the "drug dispensers" with sharp voice and pen. Soon local and state medical conventions were being held at the Sanitarium. Doctors began referring patients there, and even better, began to come themselves! Kellogg got his directors to approve an extensive advertising campaign and prepared most of the copy himself. As editor of the *Health Reformer*, he gave it a face lifting which included a new and more positive name, *Good Health*; then he used it virtually as a house organ to promote the Sanitarium.

Dr. Kellogg's desire for acceptance from his "regular" medical brethren did not lead to his watering down the main reform principles established at the Sanitarium. Drug therapy he used very sparingly, and only in exceptional circumstances. Normal procedure consisted of a variety of hydrotherapy treatments which Kellogg skillfully placed on a scientific basis. His book *Rational Hydrotherapy* became the accepted text in the field. He also placed special emphasis on corrective diet. Kellogg did not rest until he had eliminated meat from the "San" dining room. He established a special research kitchen to develop a wholesome and tasty vegetarian cuisine. He also gave major attention to corrective exercise and dress, coupled with proper rest and exposure to fresh air and sunshine.

So many changes were possible because the new chief physician was willing and anxious to work sixteen to eighteen hours a day. In addition to his medical duties, he took personal charge of training the lay staff in hydrotherapy and massage, launched a School of Hygiene to prepare health lecturers and equip them to give simple treatments, and played a major role in the business management of the Sanitarium. In his spare time, he taught classes in chemistry at the Adventists' newly launched Battle Creek College. He might even appear at an evening program to play his violin for the patients. On the evening of February 22, 1879, the patients got a special surprise. As the double doors of the main Sanitarium parlor were thrown open to the strains of Handel's *Wedding March*, the little doctor appeared with a bride on his arm. The former Ella Eaton, who had attended the School of Hygiene, was a well-educated young woman with an M.A. from Alfred University, New York. She played a devoted and efficient second violin in the doctor's life for over forty years. The first chair was always occupied by John Harvey's sense of mission to promote the "Gospel of Health."

Patronage at the Sanitarium increased rapidly. Eight months after the Kellogg era had begun, James White was ready to launch a campaign to build a new $25,000 building. One year later a five-story, 130-foot-long structure costing twice that much was dedicated. Much of the necessary construction money had to be borrowed and paid for out of Sanitarium earnings. This was symptomatic of the future. Before one debt was retired another was contracted to finance further expansion. By the end of the century, the main Sanitarium building had expanded through the addition of two wings, each about equal in size to the central part of the building. A separate charity hospital and annex had also been constructed. In addition, guests might stay in one of twenty family-size cottages the Sanitarium owned. Four hundred acres of fruit, dairy, and garden farms had been purchased to assure the institution the best possible foods. Kellogg even talked the directors into securing a resort on nearby Gougac Lake, where San patients could boat, picnic, and generally relax.

The necessity for profits to finance this continual expansion led Dr. Kellogg to pay increasing attention to wealthy patients who could stay from six weeks to three months, and who might remember the San in their wills. It also caused him to reconsider his earlier aversion to surgery. As a boy he had peered through the window while a neighborhood chum had been stretched out on the kitchen table for a minor operation. The sight of blood had nauseated him. He had experienced similar feelings while a medical student. Now, however, he recognized that some of the patients who came to the Sanitarium needed surgery. For a time, he contracted for skilled surgeons to come in from Detroit or Chicago to perform the necessary operations. But it irked Kellogg to see these men carry away fat fees and not be available to give their patients postoperative care. As quickly as possible, he traveled to New York, London, and Vienna to prepare himself in surgery. His natural quickness, skill with his hands, and sharp eye for detail, turned him into an outstanding abdominal surgeon. When he was a child, John's mother had taught him to sew; in later years he kept his fingers nimble by embroidering or crocheting while traveling on the train. Howard Kelly, the famed Johns Hopkins surgeon, credited Kellogg with "the most beautiful human needlework" he had ever seen. Substantial fees naturally resulted from Dr. Kellogg's surgery; however, they went not to enrich himself, but to pay for charity cases and Sanitarium expansion.

The rapid expansion of the Sanitarium did not meet with its founders' complete approval. Before his death in 1881, James White had already become somewhat estranged from his protege. In the next two decades Ellen White constantly cautioned against the unending expansions and additions. Among other things these placed too heavy a strain on Dr. Kellogg, she maintained. Although the little doctor had been forced to bring in a number of skilled associates, he found it difficult to share authority with any of them. Small in stature, he owned a giant-sized ego. He found it almost impossible to tolerate a man or woman who might steal too large a share of the

Dr. and Mrs. Kellogg had no children of their own, but they loved children and proved it by accepting forty-two of them into their home at different times. They adopted four or five of the children. Picture taken in 1888.

spotlight that followed him around his Sanitarium barony.

By 1900 the Sanitarium often had 700 patients in the summer months. The tendency to provide Dansville-type amusements and recreations grew stronger. This bothered Ellen White; she had long taught that mild outdoor work was better than checkers, croquet, or listening to an orchestra. Dr. Kellogg made an attempt to meet Mrs. White's objections by developing small garden plots where "San" patients could grow cabbages and potatoes, onions or flowers. It was good therapy, but few of the wealthier patrons took to the idea of being gentlemen gardeners, and the idea was never pushed as Ellen White might have wished.

By the 1890's Dr. Kellogg had grown increasingly edgy over the opposition developing toward his expansive plans in Battle Creek and his proprietary interest in other Adventist sanitariums beginning to spring up both across the nation and abroad. Frequently, he clashed over policy matters with one church leader or another. There had always been a rather large vein of suspicion in John Kellogg's personality. He now became convinced that Adventist leaders were out to "steal" the institution he had slaved to build. Some way must be found to prevent such a tragedy; ministers had no business meddling in medical affairs.

The opportunity Kellogg sought was provided by the need to secure a new charter for the Sanitarium; the original one expired at the end of thirty years. By this time, Dr. Kellogg was chairman of the Sanitarium board of directors as well as medical director. The necessary details for continuing the legal life of the institution were entrusted to his hands. He devised a new nonprofit association to hold Sanitarium properties and elect its directors, who would retain complete managerial responsibility. Stockholders in the old corporation were allowed to name one member of the new association for every share of stock held. Members of the new association did not have to be Seventh-day Adventists; in fact, it was specified that the work of the Sanitarium was to be "undenominational, unsectarian, humanitarian, and philanthropic." Although this bothered some church leaders, the fact that the original Adventist stockholders could name the members of the new association and in fact did name a substantial number of Adventist ministers, was reassuring. No one seemed to notice that Dr. Kellogg had also included in the new charter a provision allowing only those Association members actually present a voice in the annual business sessions. There was to be no more proxy voting. What this was to mean, only the future would tell.

Without warning, tragedy struck the Sanitarium on February 18, 1902. Early that morning a fire, originating in the neighborhood of the pharmacy, spread rapidly. By daylight, the entire main building with its two wings, the charity hospital, and several small adjacent structures lay in ruins. Excellent teamwork on the part of Sanitarium personnel and the local fire department made it possible to evacuate all the 400 patients safely. A single casualty resulted when an elderly patron discovered that he had forgotten his life savings and dashed into the burning building to retrieve them. Dr. Kellogg was returning from the west coast at the time and learned of the fire while changing trains in Chicago. He immediately began drawing up plans for a new building.

The struggle to rebuild proved difficult. The Sanitarium had been woefully underinsured, and Dr. Kellogg wanted to raise half a million dollars to put up the new building. Although church officials had agreed to the rebuilding and pledged their help, they now protested that Kellogg was constructing a larger, more elaborate structure than they had anticipated. Ellen White was particularly disturbed. She saw the fire as a divine judgment on the "grand hotel" atmosphere that had come to prevail at the Sanitarium. Instead of rebuilding a mammoth institution in Battle Creek, she urged, the directors should have reviewed her past counsels and established smaller sanitariums in various places.

John Kellogg could see no light in the objections being raised. Battle Creek had become synonymous with good natural health care, he said. Thousands of people all across the country looked to the Sanitarium as a beacon shining amidst the darkness of conventional medicine. Of course, the facilities must be the best! Matters were further complicated by a new book, *The Living Temple*, which Kellogg had just written. Some Adventist theologians found it permeated by a subtle pantheistic heresy. John Harvey indignantly denied their charges. He raised his own heresy cry against those church leaders who had deserted the Adventist stand on healthful living and reverted to eating meat. He further implied that the aging Ellen White was being fed misinformation about him and his work. This caused him to question the prophetic role she had long been accorded in Adventist circles.

As the months passed, the dispute festered. Finally, on November 10, 1907, the local Adventist congregation, after a trial Kellogg disdained to attend, dropped him from the church of his birth on the grounds that he had become antagonistic to its work and doctrines. The doctor professed to be too busy making sick people well to be much concerned with this action. He was determined, however, to maintain his position at the Battle Creek Sanitarium, his base of operations.

The charter provision providing that association members must be present to vote on association business now proved its power. The Adventist members of the association, especially those in the clergy, had become widely scattered after 1903, when denominational headquarters moved from Battle Creek to a suburb of Washington, D.C. At the annual Battle Creek Sanitarium Association meeting of January 16, 1909, twenty-eight Kellogg loyalists appeared out of a membership of nearly 700. At the doctor's prompting, these members exercised a right, also hidden in the Association's charter, of expelling association members no longer in harmony with the health teachings promoted at the Sanitarium. In this category were lumped all of Kellogg's principal critics within the

Dr. Kellogg began to edit Health Reformer *while attending Bellevue. Later, he changed its name to* Good Health *and made it into a Battle Creek Sanitarium house organ.*

Adventist ministry. Yet the little doctor could not quite bring himself to include the aged lady whose vision had led to the founding of the Sanitarium. Ellen White remained on the rolls of the Sanitarium Association. Perhaps he felt it unlikely that at eighty years of age she would leave the peace of her California home to arouse the faithful at an annual meeting.

So the Battle Creek Sanitarium, first in the Adventist circle of health institutions, the "fledgling water cure" which had succeeded where dozens had failed, and in the process had developed a program of preventive medicine years ahead of its time, cut its Adventist ties. Days of triumph and tribulation still lay ahead for both Kellogg and the Sanitarium, but that is another story.

An advertisement for the Sanitarium appearing in Good Health *humbly admits that "nowhere else in the world can the invalid in search of health find so great an assemblage of means and appliances for combating disease as are to be found here." Among the institution's assets listed are water of "extraordinary purity," "electric call," and "the most perfect system of sewerage that can be devised."*

The Vision Bold

BATTLE CREE

SANITARIUM

The elegant new Sanitarium building, completed in the spring of 1878, began the "grand hotel" era for the institution. Designed to be completed for $25,000, it actually cost $50,000. Before the end of the century two large wings had been added, besides a charity hospital and other buildings. Dr. Kellogg's fame spread, and more patients came. This created the need for larger buildings still, with further indebtedness.

Dr. Kellogg's genius as a writer, editor, and educator w

A demonstration that cold air from the window chills the feet, while hot air from the stove heats the upper parts. "If the gentleman could reverse his position, without inconvenience otherwise, he would secure good conditions regarding both heat and ventilation."

Recommended exercises for trunk development.

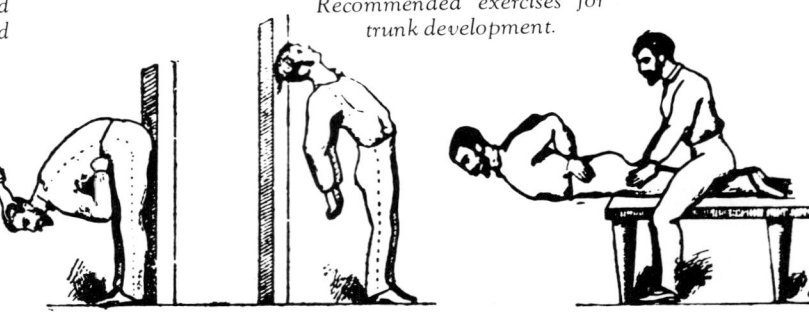

Unhealthful postures commonly seen in school classrooms.

"A remedial agent . . . readily administered with such conveniences as every family possesses."

Not a family going to sea in boats, but rubber bathtubs suggested for homes not equipped with another kind.

Dr. Kellogg's genius as a writer, editor, and educator w

one whit less than his skill as a physician and surgeon

One treatment for nosebleed, using "cotton-wool or soft, dry muslin."

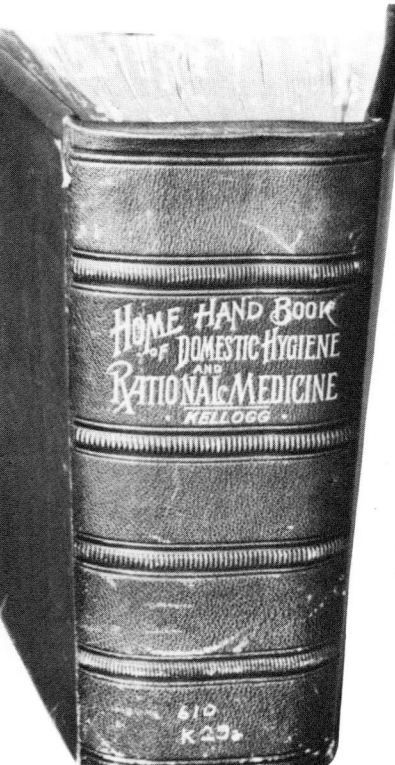

The doctor's verbal output, spoken and written, was prodigious, and some of his books sold into the hundreds of thousands. Home Handbook, one of his many books, was encyclopedic in scope, containing 1672 pages. His writing style was vigorous, folksy, opinionated, often interspersed with illustrations from his own medical practice and his voracious reading. He possessed an amazing breadth of knowledge of the medical science of his time.

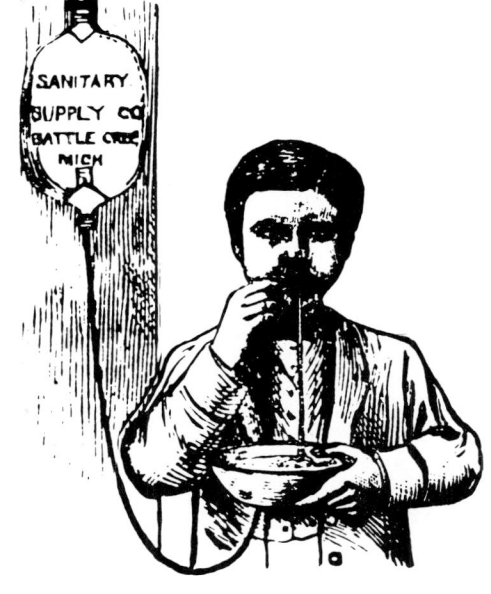

"Much benefit may be derived by the proper use of this bath in case of acute or chronic catarrh."

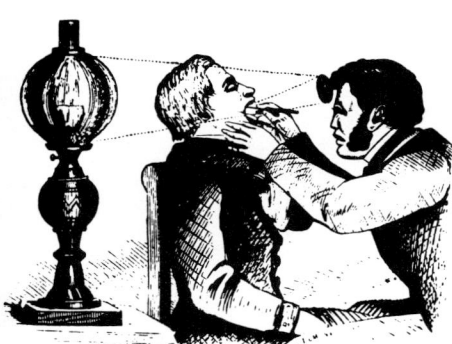

"By means of . . . the laryngoscope . . . it is possible to inspect the larynx and even the upper part of the trachea."

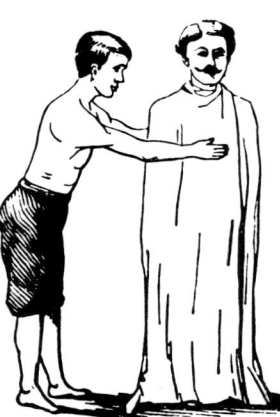

"Especially applicable to cases in which there is defective circulation in the extremities, inactive skin and liver, and nervousness."

"The wheel carriage . . . is a very useful apparatus, by the use of which a patient suffering with disease of the spine may be able to take a considerable amount of exercise in the open air."

The Vision Bold

Widely sought as a speaker and lecturer,

Monday Night Medical Question Box talks at the sanitarium attracted audiences of seventy-five to two hundred guests from all over the country and abroad.

Kellogg's writings excoriated not only alcohol and tobacco but also tea and coffee. "Rum Blossom," "A Tea Toper," and "Smoker's Cancer" helped illustrate his voluminous Home Hand Book of Domestic Hygiene and Rational Medicine.

llogg educated thousands in "biologic" living

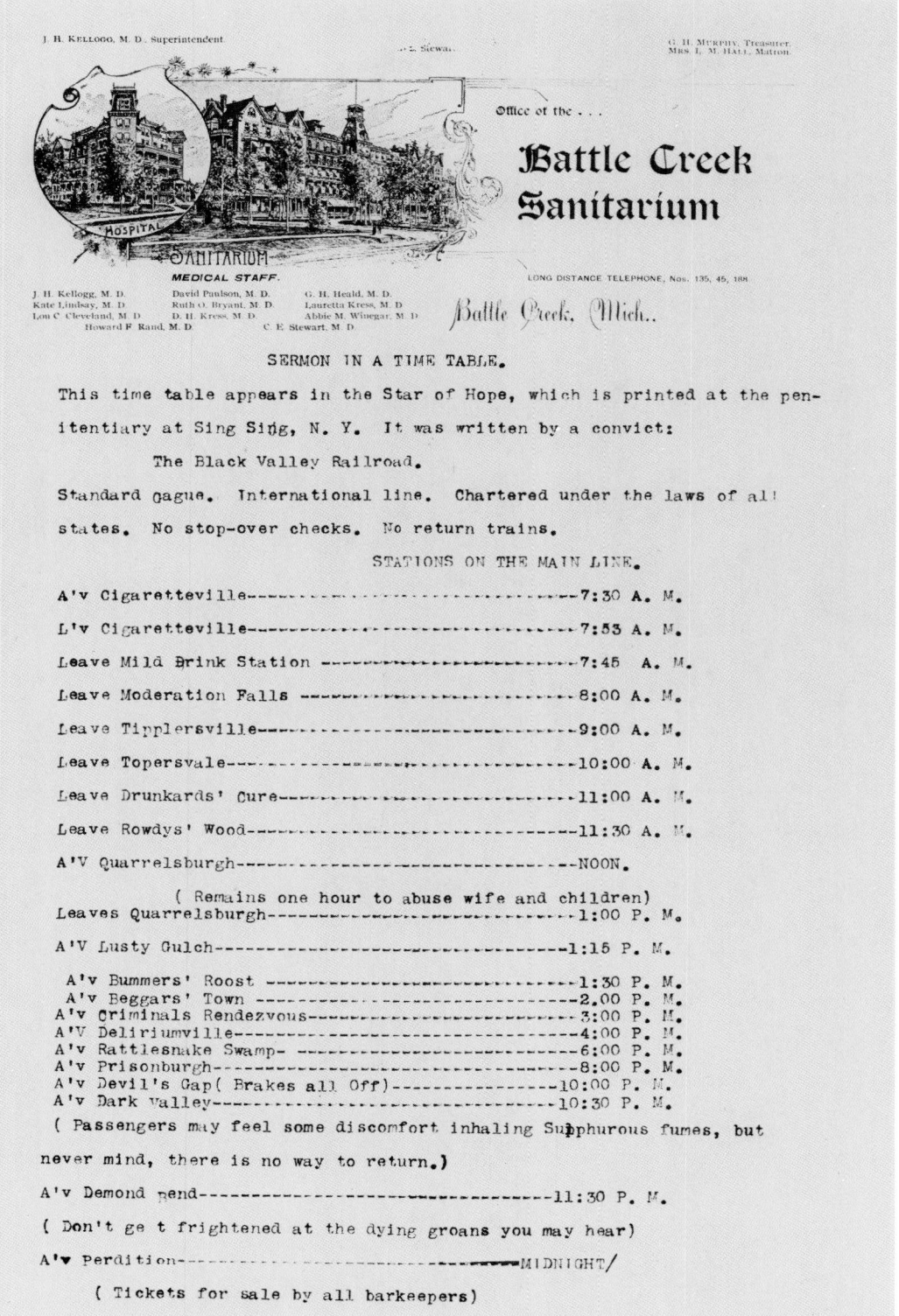

In the late 1890's, the doctor circulated "Sermon in a Time Table" to patients. Borrowed from a Sing Sing prison paper, it portrayed the downward road of the intemperate from Cigaretteville through Quarrelsburgh, Deliriumville, Devil's Gap, and Demon's Bend to Perdition, the final destination.

Sanitarium patients learned that exerc[ise] serves as a tonic

s digestion, helps control obesity, and
d and nerves

Dr. John Harvey strongly urged measured exercise, especially recommending walking, cycling, and swimming. He rode his own bicycle into his ninetieth year. The doctor often stopped sanitarium employees and patients to tell them how to sit, stand, and walk.

Not a scene from Tchaikowsky's "Swan Lake," but the exercise idea catching on at Battle Creek—to the accompaniment of music.

The Vision Bold

Ladies' day at Battle Creek Sanitarium swimming pool produced a pleasing eyeful of swimwear fashions. Kellogg devoutly promoted swimming as one of the best forms of exercise.

"Let's see—how do you begin this thing? Oh yes, raise left foot high, higher."

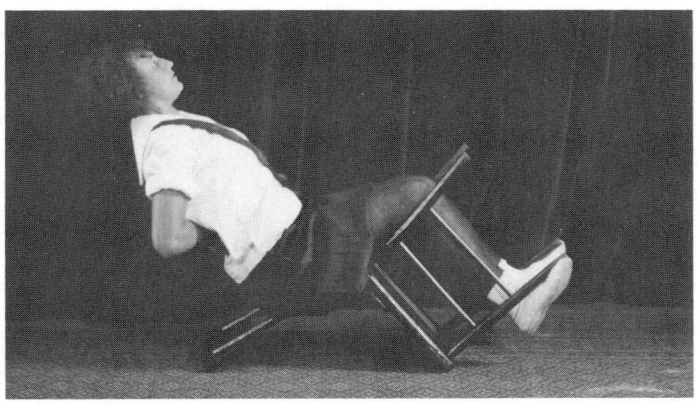

"I think I'm going to break in two at the middle, but it's supposed to help the tummy muscles."

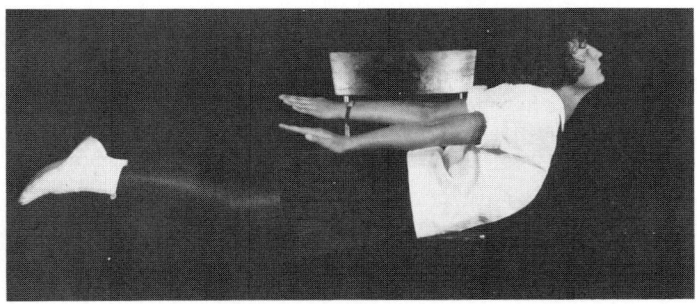

"Look at me now—I can fly like a bird!"

"Well, that's enough for once. Exercise is really wonderful, I guess."

The Vision Bold

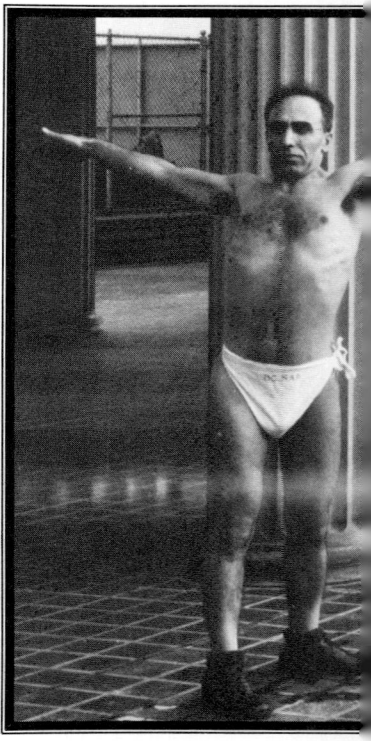

Above: At a mass calisthenics workout for small fry, the ubiquitous little doctor, dressed in his standard white, showed up for an inspection, and no doubt delivered a pep talk on the virtues of exercise. Right: Men dressed in a reasonable facsimile of the diaper exercise on the Towers Addition rooftop, the final addition to the huge sanitarium.

BATTLE CREEK SANITARIUM BECAME A SOCIAL CENTER, A MECCA, THE PLACE TO GO

Above: The famous physician welcomes the opportunity to educate a group of distinguished ladies on the merits of biologic living. Through the years he entertained John Burroughs, Thomas Edison, Eddie Cantor, J. C. Penney, Wilfred Grenfell, Johnny Weismuller, Amelia Earhart, Ivan Pavlov, Henry Ford, George Bernard Shaw, Luther Burbank, Richard E. Byrd, William Howard Taft, others.

Left: Kellogg was the personification of the work ethic, a human dynamo, always energetic, always busy. A lover of innovation, he held the first known transatlantic medical consultation by telephone, advising a physician in Monte Carlo.

The Vision Bold

The Residence, with twenty roon

The Kelloggs moved into The Residence, five blocks west of the sanitarium, in 1894. Its spacious grounds included a grove of trees, deer park, vegetable gardens, and a large children's playground.

For several years after his wife's death, the doctor continued to include her picture on his Christmas cards.

70

came home to forty-two children

Dr. Kellogg's wife, the former Ella Eaton of Alfred Center, New York, was a lifelong Seventh Day Baptist. Cultured and educated, she served on the editorial staff of Good Health magazine for forty-three years and also wrote several books. She spent much of her time and strength caring for the numerous foster children in their home. One of her best friends was Ellen White.

The Vision Bold

The $4 million Towers Addition—final convuls

Will Success Spoil John Kellogg?

owth spurt of a once-modest health center

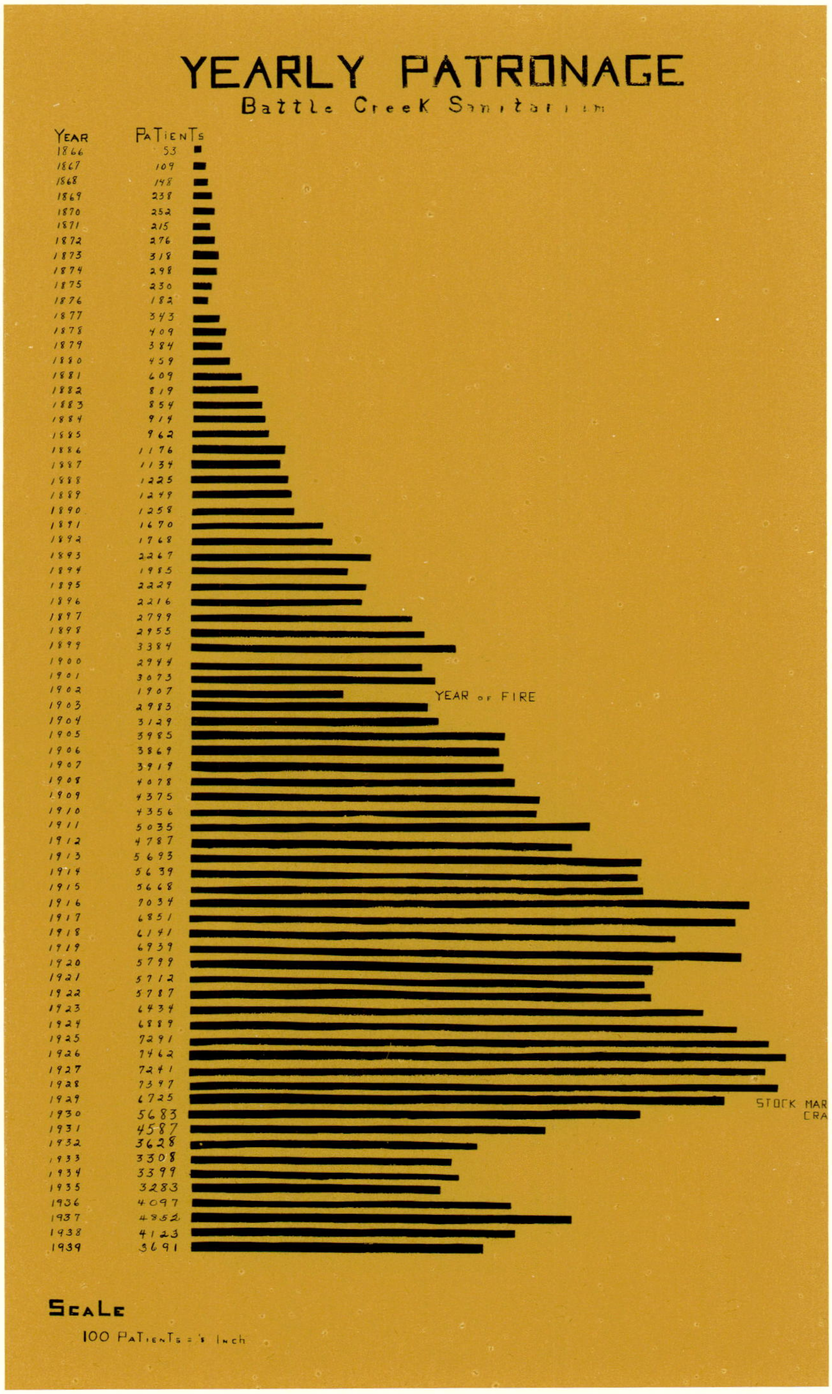

Started in 1927, the Towers Addition expanded sanitarium facilities to accommodate 1,300 guests. Then came 1929 and the depression. The average number of patients fell to 300 in 1930, and in 1933 the institution went into receivership. The Federal Government eventually turned it into an Army hospital, then the national headquarters for Civil Defense. Battle Creek Sanitarium moved to smaller quarters.

YEARLY PATRONAGE
Battle Creek Sanitarium

Year	Patients
1866	53
1867	109
1868	148
1869	238
1870	252
1871	215
1872	276
1873	318
1874	298
1875	230
1876	182
1877	343
1878	409
1879	384
1880	459
1881	609
1882	819
1883	854
1884	919
1885	962
1886	1176
1887	1134
1888	1225
1889	1249
1890	1258
1891	1670
1892	1768
1893	2267
1894	1985
1895	2229
1896	2216
1897	2799
1898	2955
1899	3384
1900	2944
1901	3073
1902	1907
1903	2983
1904	3129
1905	3985
1906	3869
1907	3919
1908	4078
1909	4375
1910	4356
1911	5035
1912	4787
1913	5693
1914	5639
1915	5668
1916	7034
1917	6851
1918	6141
1919	6939
1920	5799
1921	5712
1922	5787
1923	6434
1924	6889
1925	7291
1926	7462
1927	7241
1928	7397
1929	6725
1930	5683
1931	4587
1932	3628
1933	3308
1934	3399
1935	3283
1936	4097
1937	4852
1938	4123
1939	3691

YEAR OF FIRE

STOCK MARKET CRASH

Scale
100 Patients = 1 Inch

Will Keith Kellogg, at left, with friend Will Shepard. From a tintype made in Kalamazoo in 1877.

GRANOLA, POSTUM, CORN FLAKES, AND PEANUT BUTTER

SOMETHING NEW IS STIRRING UP IN BATTLE CREEK KITCHENS

Battle Creek did not become the cereal capital of the world by chance. Nor was it a happenstance that from this small Michigan city came both the first peanut butter and the first vegetable protein foods specifically designed to resemble meat. These developments and others are traceable to Dr. John Harvey Kellogg's commitment to improving the eating habits of Battle Creek Sanitarium patients and those of his fellow Seventh-day Adventists. As his vision broadened and the profitability of some items became apparent to others, the dream expanded. Some dared to think of changing the eating habits of mankind — and they partially succeeded.

Since Colonial days Americans had depended heavily on meat as a major item in their diet. In his classic picture of American society at the opening of the nineteenth century, Henry Adams notes the prevalence of salt pork at every meal. Other staples included potatoes, cornmeal in mush or puddings, and molasses; all were washed down by liberal amounts of coffee or tea. Even after Americans no longer endured the rigors of frontier life or the twelve-hour day in the factories, old habits of eating persisted. Small wonder that Battle Creek Sanitarium patients often complained of dyspepsia!

After her vision in Otsego, Michigan, Ellen White persistently pointed Seventh-day Adventists to the virtues of a vegetarian diet. Fruits, grains, and nuts had been man's original bill of fare, she reminded them. With the addition of vegetables, modest amounts of dairy products, and a few eggs from "healthy" hens, it still best served his needs. All of this John Kellogg had accepted as a youth. Even while boarding himself as a medical student in New York City, Kellogg had practiced a "reform" diet. He had lived principally on graham crackers and apples, with an occasional baked potato or coconut to add variety. His limited time and cooking facilities had not allowed him to prepare cooked wheat, oats, rice, or other grains. He had no place to keep fresh vegetables or fruits even if they had been available and he could have afforded them. Still he had maintained good health and gained seventeen pounds on what must have been a monotonous diet.

Years later at the Battle Creek Sanitarium, Dr. Kellogg soon found that keeping paying patients happy on a radically different diet was quite different from disciplining himself. At the outset, he wisely refrained from imposing a ban on meat. Instead, he attempted by his personal example in the dining room to show the "better way." It wasn't enough. Patients professed a willingness to try the vegetables and grains Kellogg ate, but complained of their monotony. Something had to be done.

Kellogg turned to a heavier reliance on bread and other wheat products. Sylvester Graham had promoted whole wheat as a panacea thirty years earlier, and Graham's writings had made their impact on Kellogg. With the aid of Mrs. Kellogg, the doctor soon had the Sanitarium bakery producing a tempting variety of breads and crackers. Some of these were laced with dried fruits; others included oatmeal, rice flour, or a variety of whole grains. As his studies in food chemistry progressed, Dr. Kellogg became aware of certain problems connected with the consumption of whole grains. These foods possessed a high starch content, which meant slower digestion. Kellogg also learned that prolonged baking started the dextrinization of starches, the first step in their digestion. This led him to an emphasis on zwieback, twice-baked bread.

At Dansville, New York, Dr. Jackson, who had also been influenced by Graham, was producing probably the first cold cereal breakfast food. He called it Granula. In reality, Granula was simply Graham flour made from "Genesee Valley white winter wheat," mixed with water and baked in sheets in a slow oven. Later, this thin unleavened bread was broken up, rebaked, and ground into small pieces about the size of modern Grape-Nuts. To be edible, Granula needed to be soaked for at least twenty minutes in milk or cream. Many preferred to let it stand overnight in a bowl of whole milk in a cool icebox.

Dr. Kellogg decided to try an adaptation of the Dansville product at the Sanitarium. He added cornmeal and oatmeal in various amounts to Graham flour until a product with satisfactory taste appeal emerged. Kellogg baked and ground up his cereal like Granula, and he acknowledged his debt to Jackson by calling the Battle Creek cereal Granola. Dansville people caused rumblings of legal action, but the name stuck. Kellogg's attempts to secure grain products that were tasty as well as healthful paid off. Not only did patients complain less over the menus, but more and more of them sent back to the Sanitarium for supplies of Granola or a favorite fruit cracker after they had returned home.

Even before Dr. Kellogg launched a new era at the old Western Health Reform Institute, earlier managers had developed an imitation coffee from a mixture of roasted bran and molasses. Known as Caramel Cereal Coffee, it also owed a debt to Dansville, where Dr. Jackson had produced a concoction named "Somo." Not that Jackson was all that original; frontier women and Civil War soldiers, unable to get real coffee, had long before found that burned wheat and molasses made a tolerable substitute. Kellogg had no enthusiasm for Caramel Cereal Coffee, but patients denied the real product demanded some kind of hot drink. Here again he found it profitable to tinker with the original formula, and again a substantial mail-order business developed.

The more Dr. Kellogg studied the process of digestion, the more convinced he became that good digestion begins in the mouth with food that is thoroughly chewed. Observing that most people gulped their food, Kellogg set out to devise some way to slow down the eating habits of his patients. He fastened on the idea of requiring each to start his meal by slowly chewing a couple of pieces of zwieback or a dry Granola "cocktail." The hard nature of these foods precluded speed, and by requiring them at the start of a meal, the doctor hoped to induce a pattern of eating that would continue right through dessert. Through a combination of events, this eating formula launched Kellogg on the search which ended with the first cereal flakes.

One morning John Kellogg found himself confronted by an obviously upset lady patient. Putting on his most conciliatory manner, he

Sylvester Graham (1794-1851), American food reformer whose name became synonymous with whole wheat.

attempted to calm the woman. To his chagrin, he discovered that she had cracked her dental plate while following his recommended first course at breakfast. The lady suggested, in what he hoped was a joking manner, that he owed her at least $10 to repair the damages. Immediately, the orders went out to the experimental kitchen: Start hunting for a way in which grain products can be baked for dextrinization and yet be more soluble.

Before long, some of Dr. Kellogg's patients had heard of his new interest. One lady shared with the doctor a new product she had received from a friend in Denver, a little pillow made from strands of boiled wheat. Kellogg was intrigued with this creation which its inventor, Henry Perky, called Shredded Whole Wheat Bread. Perky had become interested in foods for the practical reason that he had digestive troubles. As a result of reading, he became convinced of the advantages of eating wheat instead of meat. Being of an inventive turn of mind, he proceeded to boil and steam a batch of wheat, after which he ran it through a short pair of rollers, one of which was grooved. The resulting strands of wheat piled up to make the soft, puffy pillows.

Kellogg managed to get a large enough sample of Perky's wheat pillows to try in the Sanitarium dining room. The patients reacted negatively. They complained that the new product lacked taste appeal and was difficult to chew. Some said it was "like eating a whisk broom." Still the doctor was interested enough to stop off and see Perky in Denver while on a trip to the west coast. One of the problems with Shredded Wheat Bread was that its high moisture content caused it to spoil rather quickly. Perky had about given up on marketing the product, and had decided simply to sell machines for making it. Kellogg left Denver with the promise of a machine for the Sanitarium, but it never arrived. Probably John Harvey's enthusiasm for baking grain products had triggered a new idea in Perky. Soon he was baking his wheat pillows and finding that this solved the storage problem. After a couple of false starts in Massachusetts, Perky eventually located his production operations in the shadow of Niagara Falls, where he harvested a great deal of free publicity among the thousands who visited America's chief scenic attraction.

Unhappy over Perky's failure to provide the promised shredding machine, Dr. Kellogg also blamed himself for not buying out Perky's

W. K. Kellogg in 1861 at the age of one.

Will Kellogg with four of his brothers and sisters, in 1866. Left to right: Preston S., Emma, W.K., Clara, John Harvey, Laura.

Will Kellogg at the age of fourteen.

entire operation. He redoubled his search for a new, attractive, easily edible form of whole wheat. He began to carry on a variety of experiments in Ella Kellogg's big kitchen at night. He dreamed of being able to turn each grain of wheat into a tiny flake of toast. To accomplish this, he borrowed a pair of rollers Mrs. Kellogg used to roll out pastry crusts. After soaking some wheat, he put it through the rollers; a mixture of watery starch and coarse bran was the result. Kellogg then tried boiling and steaming the wheat for various periods of time. All he got was a pasty mess which clung to the rollers.

One night, just as he had finished cooking a batch of wheat, the doctor was called away for several hours. He left the wheat sitting on the back of the stove. When Kellogg returned, he was about to throw the old batch of wheat out and start again, but decided to run it through the rollers and see what would happen. To his surprise, each kernel of wheat flattened out on the rollers. Calling one of his foster children to aid him, he soon had the youngster scraping the flakes from the rollers with a large bread knife.

Dr. Kellogg still did not understand what had caused the change, but he felt close to success. He transferred the experiments to the big Sanitarium kitchen, where Will Keith Kellogg, the doctor's young brother, now became his chief collaborator. For years, W. K. had been serving as John's bookkeeper, business manager, purchasing agent, and "man Friday." Now, at the end of a long day's work, the two brothers pried together into a secret of the flakes. For some time, they knew only failure. Then one day it happened again. Events prevented their running a batch of cooked wheat through the rollers for about 48 hours. By that time, the wheat was moldy, but they decided to process it anyway. To their surprise, flakes, larger and thinner than the previous time, resulted. Spread out on baking sheets and toasted in the oven, they proved crisp and edible—if one ignored their slightly moldy flavor.

The brothers discovered the value of letting the boiled wheat stand for a time. During this "tempering" time, the moisture had a chance to equalize throughout the wheat berry. But how long to wait? They made more experiments. Changing atmospheric conditions made a difference, too. Meanwhile, W. K. secured an old paper-cutting knife from the Review and Herald Publishing Association. A local mechanic helped them to fasten the knife so that it scraped the flakes from the rollers without damaging them. Dr. Kellogg was much too busy with his medical work to carry on the many experiments necessary to discover the correct tempering time and work out other production problems. This job fell to W. K. The doctor still provided ideas, and the younger brother tried out some of his own as well. Gradually, they developed a smooth, efficient system for making the flakes.

On the last day of May, 1894, Dr. Kellogg filed for a patent on flaked cereals and the process for making them. The patent covered manufacture of flakes from barley, oats, corn, and other grains as well as wheat, but they made no attempt at this time to produce other than the wheat flakes. The rollers then available were just not strong enough to crush corn or rice satisfactorily. Besides, wheat was the king of cereals in Dr. Kellogg's estimation. He named the new product Granose Flakes—*gran* from grain, and *ose*, a chemical suffix indicating a partially digested food.

After all their difficulties developing wheat flakes, Dr. Kellogg felt unsure about public acceptance. He ordered a large batch of the flakes rubbed through a sieve, so that they became a coarse meal which mushed up instantly in milk. These he labeled Granose Grits. Will Kellogg was horrified. "Keep the flakes," he implored. The older brother remained skeptical until he found out that the Sanitarium patients agreed with W.K.—almost unanimously!

As with Granola, the Kelloggs first intended Granose Flakes for use only at the Sanitarium. But, as with other San foods, a mail-order business gradually developed. A little later, Dr. Kellogg agreed to a demonstration of the flakes in some of the larger stores in the Chicago area. This resulted in more sales. In turn, production facilities had to be increased. Here the Sanitarium directors balked. As a consequence, the doctor formed his own Sanitas Company to produce flaked cereals and other food products he was already dreaming of. Brother Will handled the business end of Sanitas, receiving a 25 percent share of the profits.

During the 1890's, ideas for food products seemed to shoot out from John Kellogg's mind like sparks from a Fourth of July sparkler. The problem of correct amounts of protein for persons giving up meat concerned him. As a substitute for meat, Kellogg recommended a larger use of legumes—dried peas, beans, peanuts. Yet these foods created problems for many

Granola, Postum, Corn Flakes, and Peanut Butter

As a broom salesman for his father's factory, Will Kellogg traveled over a wide area of Michigan. A hard worker and a good manager, he saved $1,000 from his earnings when he was seventeen.

people. Beans, for instance, frequently caused gas pains, for which Kellogg prescribed the chewing of charcoal tablets. But even the charismatic Dr. Kellogg made very few converts to charcoal tablets. There were those who complained that peanuts irritated their digestive tracts. John Harvey maintained that this happened because they failed to chew the peanuts well enough, but he found it even more difficult to change people's chewing habits than their dietary tastes.

The answer, of course, was peanut butter. Just when or how this product first was tried is a matter of dispute. One story credits with the discovery an unnamed young Sanitarium worker employed to roast peanuts for the patients. According to this account, Dr. Kellogg chanced upon the young peanut roaster talking to his girl friend instead of working at his job, and he proceeded to lecture the boy about honest work. Irritated and embarrassed, the lad sought to relieve his frustration by taking a nearby hammer and smashing a peanut. To his surprise the peanut, instead of flying into bits, sort of "mushed up." The boy repeated his act on several other peanuts with similar results. Scraping the smashed nuts into a little ball, he presented it to the doctor the next morning. Kellogg's eyes lit up. "I'll give you fifty dollars for it!" Thus peanut butter was born—or so one story goes.

W. K. Kellogg remembered a less dramatic beginning. One day Dr. Kellogg had sent word for his younger brother to get a batch of peanuts, remove the hulls, and run them through the flaking rollers. Ten pounds of nuts thus processed produced the first batch of peanut butter, which was sold largely to Seventh-day Adventists. Whoever created the product, and however, Dr. Kellogg made no effort to patent the soon-to-be-popular spread. As he explained it, this was something he believed "the world ought to have; let everybody that wants it have it and make the best use of it."

His zeal to win men and women to a vegetarian diet did not blind John Kellogg to the fact that steak, chops, and roasts held a powerful appeal to most Americans. He needed to develop something from vegetable sources which would actually look and taste a great deal like a beef roast. His first creation promoted commercially, called Nuttose, appeared in 1896. Subsequently, other products, of which Protose has remained the most popular, appeared at intervals. These substitute meats contained varying combinations of wheat gluten, peanut meal, and flavorings. Whether or not the Nuttose line of foods tasted "like the real thing," their nutritional value was freely conceded. Looking ahead at a rapidly expanding population, Dr. Kellogg predicted that in the years ahead Americans could not

Will Kellogg at the age of thirty, and wife, the former Ella "Puss" Davis.

afford the luxury of feeding twenty pounds of grain to get one pound of meat. Recent meat and grain shortages seem to confirm the accuracy of his prophecy.

Not all of the doctor's food innovations caught on. At about the same time that he was seeking a meat substitute, Kellogg also tested his first artificial milk. "Malted Nuts" was a powdered form of almonds and peanuts which could be mixed with water. Despite a testimonial from Clara Barton, and despite the doctor's claim that Malted Nuts was better than cows' milk in cases of "biliousness, hyperpepsia, and nervous headache," the beverage failed to attract a following. Many years later, Kellogg had more success making a milk from soybeans.

In spite of Will Kellogg's urgings, his doctor brother refused to let Will launch a major advertising campaign for Sanitas products. John was always reluctant to spend money for certain things, and he also feared lest his fellow physicians misconstrue his commercial ventures either as personal advertising or as promotion of patent-medicine type remedies. Then a brash ex-Sanitarium patient showed the Kelloggs there could be real money in a health food.

Charles W. Post was not quite forty in 1891, when his train pulled into Battle Creek. Already, he had gone through several bankruptcies and at least three physical breakdowns. He had been partner in a hardware store in Missouri, sold real estate and run a woolen mill in Texas, and manufactured farm equipment in Illinois. After each financial reverse, his health had also nosedived, and he had found no lasting cure. Now he had come to see what the famed Battle Creek Sanitarium could do. Hard up for funds, he paid his bills for the first several months with blankets salvaged from his Texas woolen mill. Mrs. Post also took a new type of suspenders C. W. had invented and peddled them from house to house in Battle Creek. The Kelloggs later claimed that Post had been given reduced rates as a semicharity patient at the Sanitarium.

Nine months of Sanitarium treatments left no visible improvement in Post's health, but it did leave him with an antagonism toward Dr. Kellogg and his theories. It also left him with an idea that turned him into a multimillionaire. While at the "San", Post had shown intense interest in the experimental kitchen where workers tinkered with the Caramel Cereal Coffee formula. Growing suspicious, the Sanitarium matron spoke to the doctor about it, telling him she feared Post intended to steal the recipe and sell his own brand. Should she keep Post away from the kitchen?

"No, indeed," Kellogg replied. He explained that the more cereal coffee people drank, the less they would consume of the real thing. He

Charles W. Post, of "Postum" fame, learned secrets of food processing in Battle Creek Sanitarium kitchens. One of the few mistakes Post made was "Elijah's Manna," which drew the wrath of offended clergymen. He renamed the cereal Post Toasties.

wanted reform, not profits. (Especially so, when he had no idea the profits could run into millions!)

After Post stopped treatments at the Sanitarium, he tried Christian Science and mental suggestion, effecting his own cure at last, he said, simply by telling himself he was well. Moving to the opposite side of Battle Creek, he opened a medical boardinghouse known as LaVita Inn where he practiced mental therapeutics and offered a diet free of coffee, tea, and whiskey. Post claimed a number of cures involving ailments from rheumatism to erysipelas. But Charlie Post was at heart a promoter, and the idea for a cereal coffee had been rattling around in his head.

On New Year's Day, 1895, Post cooked up his first large batch of what he modestly named Postum—a mixture of wheat, beans, and molasses. Battle Creek residents remained notably unimpressed, but Charlie Post adopted two merchandising concepts which made his product click: delayed billing which allowed merchants to stock Postum and pay for it out of their sales, and massive local advertising. The advertising smacked more than a little of the patent medicine man. A Post-discovered disease suddenly appeared: coffee neuralgia. The remedy was simple; lay off the coffee and drink Postum. A catchy slogan highlighted ads and labels: "It Makes Red Blood." How better could one appeal to red-blooded Americans?

In the second year of operation, Postum grossed over a quarter million dollars in sales; two years later the figure had trebled. Noticing that Postum sales were especially brisk during cold weather, its manufacturer decided to make a complementary product for the warm months. Again, he came up with a food that resembled an old Sanitarium standby. For several years, the Posts had concocted a homemade type of Granola for their own use. Now C. W. decided that it, too, had a commercial future. Three years after the birth of Postum, Grape-Nuts went into production, its name taken from maltose, or "grape sugar" as Post called it, and from its nutlike flavor.

The same imaginative advertising Post had used with Postum, he now turned loose on Grape-Nuts. It was a great brain food; it tightened loose teeth; it benefited victims of malaria and tuberculosis! Within ten years of his arrival in Battle Creek, Post was clearing one million dollars a year. The success of the man W. K. Kellogg termed "the original imitator" was not lost on a host of would-be competitors. Battle Creek was about to enter the Great Cereal Boom.

Just after the turn of the century, the boom began. At first, neither cereal coffees nor granulated foods like Grape-Nuts captured center

Post started making Postum in 1895, and by 1900 his food factory was netting $3 million.

stage. Rather, it was wheat flakes. First on the scene was the Battle Creek Pure Food Company, producers of Malta Vita. Their basic innovation was to add barley malt syrup, a Post discovery, to the standard wheat flake which they learned to produce by luring a bakery foreman away from the Kelloggs' Sanitas Company. Sales mushroomed overnight, and collapsed nearly as fast when sloppy production policies resulted in flakes that turned moldy on grocery shelves. Malta Vita's experience was typical of many others: Force, Cero-Fruto, Mapl-Flakes, Norka Malted Oats. Over forty cereal manufacturing companies organized in Battle Creek within a couple of years. But in less than a decade they had disappeared, most without a trace, a few absorbed by the Ralston Purina Company or Quaker Oats. The two originals, Kellogg and Post, alone remained.

The cereal boom had not hurt Post, but it had played havoc with the profits of the Sanitas Company. A $22,000 profit in 1895 had turned into a loss by 1902. It was not the competition alone that had hurt Sanitas. To Will Kellogg's despair, his doctor brother showed more interest in dreaming up new food creations than in authorizing the concerted advertising, sales, and production efforts needed to capitalize on the appeal of any one of them. Always one to pinch his pennies, John Kellogg could not accept the idea that one must spend money in order to earn it. These were years, too, when he was preoccupied with his growing feud with the Adventist leadership. He couldn't concentrate on selling wheat or corn flakes.

By now, Dr. Kellogg had learned to resent the competition. As much as anything, he was angry at companies who bribed key Sanitas employees into leaving with production techniques and food formulas neatly stowed away in their heads. A lawsuit against the makers of Malta Vita, however, turned out disastrously. The courts ruled that small changes in formula or production techniques were sufficient to protect Malta Vita's patents. After this reverse, Dr. Kellogg lost heart. He was still angry enough to allow

Will Kellogg left his brother's employ and formed the Battle Creek Toasted Corn Flake Company.

Will to take a swipe at the competition by printing what was to become a famous slogan on all Granose Flake boxes: "Beware of imitation. None genuine without this signature—W. K. Kellogg." Probably the doctor hoped to gain some advantage by connecting his famous name with Sanitas products without being subject to attack from the medical fraternity for unorthodox advertising.

The early months of the twentieth century saw an increasing tenseness develop between the Kellogg brothers. For years, W. K. had put up with a host of indignities at the hands of his imperious brother. The time came when a new factory must be built to produce Granose Flakes. When the building was completed, Dr. Kellogg said he had not authorized its construction—Will had. It would be up to W. K. to pay the $50,000 cost, the doctor declared. That, plus differences over some Sanitarium matters, must have seemed like the last straws to Will Kellogg. He notified the doctor he was quitting at the "San." But after the 1902 fire, he relented and for two years and a half carried a major load in financing its rebuilding.

In 1898, the Kellogg brothers had developed the first corn flakes, yet for the next five years they had done very little with the discovery. Made from whole corn without any flavorings, the flakes were thick and tasteless. Then the brothers discovered that substituting corn grits for whole corn resulted in a thinner flake; and the addition of malt improved the flavor. While John Harvey was in Europe, W. K. made a daring move; he added some sugar to the formula and found the taste better yet. John Harvey was furious, but sales increased to 150 cases of corn flakes per day, and the sugar stayed in.

Dr. Kellogg may not have understood the secrets for Charlie Post's financial success; W. K. did, and he yearned to try them out on corn flakes. The only way to do this, W. K. decided, was to form a new company and buy from the doctor the right to manufacture corn flakes. Since the patents on the flaking process had been declared invalid, W. K. might simply have formed his company and begun making flakes, but this he considered dishonest. With the help of some St. Louis businessmen who had learned to respect his judgment at the Sanitarium, Will formed the Battle Creek Toasted Corn Flake Company in February, 1906. After months of negotiating, John Harvey had finally agreed to sell corn flake rights to his brother's company in exchange for $22,400 in cash and the largest block of stock in the new concern. It was none too soon. Already Charlie Post had come out with a corn flake he called "Elijah's Manna." It was an unfortunate choice of name; people considered it sacrilegious. By the time Post caught on and changed the name to Post Toasties, W. K. was well on the way to cornering the corn flake trade.

Dr. Kellogg proceeded to scatter some of his Toasted Corn Flakes stock around to San employees as bonuses in lieu of a pay raise. Patiently, and quietly, W. K. picked the shares up at bargain prices until he had majority control of the corporation. Then, severing his connections with Sanitas, W. K. started to make and sell corn flakes in earnest. Six months after the birth of his company he bought his first full-page ad in *Ladies' Home Journal*, and one of the most imaginative advertising campaigns in history had begun. A few months later, ladies in New York, Chicago, and St. Louis were invited through major newspaper ads to "wink" at their grocer on Wednesday and see what they got. A box of Kellogg's Toasted Corn Flakes, of course. (Reasoning that "Sanitas" sounded like a disinfectant, Will had decided to drop it as part of the name and substitute "Kellogg's.") Within weeks, corn flakes sales in New York City alone had zoomed from two carloads a month to a carload per day!

Shortly after W. K. had dropped the name Sanitas, Dr. Kellogg also decided to drop "Sanitas" and establish a new Kellogg Food Company in its place. The alleged reason was to forestall a "Professor" Frank Kellogg (no relation), who was marketing a weight-reducing patent medicine in Battle Creek, from getting into the food business and causing confusion and embarrassment. When the doctor further decided to add the Kellogg name to all the food products his company made, W. K. became suspicious that John Harvey had other reasons for the name change. Will saw this as a cheap way to profit by the hundreds of thousands of dollars'

Two brothers, two geniuses, both world-famous. A physician who knew them both well remarked, "John Harvey Kellogg and W. K. Kellogg were like two fellows trying to climb the same ladder at the same time." The brothers did not resemble each other either in appearance or temperament.

worth of advertising purchased to promote Kellogg's Toasted Corn Flakes!

The Kellogg brothers now began a struggle in the courts that was to last for over a decade, embittering their personal relationship for most of the rest of their lives. W. K.'s wrath had been kindled earlier when John Harvey had printed on all Sanitas wheat flake cartons that his was the "only flaked product which has a legitimate pedigree." Now when the threat of bringing out a competitive wheat flake failed to convince Dr. Kellogg to drop the name Kellogg's from his products, Will offered his brother $50,000 to discontinue the use of the family name on his foods. At first, John Harvey agreed, but when a contract to that effect was brought for his signature he changed his mind.

At last, in the late summer of 1910, Will filed suit to have the doctor enjoined from using the name Kellogg either as a descriptive food name or as part of his company name. Will's lawyers claimed that the elder brother deliberately

sought to benefit from over $2,000,000 of advertising purchased by W. K.'s company. They also maintained that the doctor's salesmen misrepresented his products, intimating that they were produced by the makers of Kellogg's Toasted Corn Flakes.

Once so shy about seeing the Kellogg name on his food innovations, John Harvey now claimed that it was his work and reputation which gave the family name value in any kind of advertising. Will disagreed violently. The marketing of 50,000,000 boxes of corn flakes with his signature on the box should have convinced the public that more than one Kellogg in Battle Creek had something to do with food! At last, the warring brothers reached an out-of-court compromise. The doctor agreed to drop the name "Kellogg's" from his food products, but was allowed to keep it as part of his company name.

This temporary truce did not prevent W. K. from taking gleeful advantage of John Harvey whenever possible. One such incident involved a multigrain cereal which Dr. Kellogg had developed and started to market under the name "Pep." It was a catchy name, but when he came to file for the trademark, he found that a small producer of a popcorn and candy confection in New York City already owned it. The doctor offered to buy the trademark for $5,000; the owner asked $7,500. Although he was making about $2,000 per day profit on his Pep, John Harvey always wanted a bargain. He continued to haggle with the New York owner. Meanwhile, W. K. learned of the bargaining, sent his New York lawyer around, and snapped up the Pep trademark. When the doctor finally decided to pay the $7,500, he found that "Pep" was no longer for sale. He shifted the name of his latest creation to "Zo," the Greek word for life, but somehow that never caught on. Perhaps the American public was not sophisticated enough in 1915.

Family name troubles surfaced once more with a battle over "bran." Since 1908, the doctor's company had sold granulated bran as a natural laxative for mixing with other breakfast cereals. By 1914, it was selling at the rate of 100,000 boxes per year. Early in 1915, Dr. Kellogg decided to shorten the name of his packaged bran from "Battle Creek Diet System Sterilized Bran" to "Kellogg's Sterilized Bran." He claimed that this did not violate his agreement with Will as that agreement had covered only flaked grains. The new name, plus a vigorous advertising campaign, resulted in a jump in sales to 250,000 boxes of bran in 1915 and 600,000 in 1916. W. K. decided to fight fire with fire. In the fall of 1915, he brought out Kellogg's Toasted Bran Flakes and followed it six months later with his own "Kellogg's Bran" in granular form. Confusion reigned in grocery stores!

Now it was Dr. Kellogg's turn to bring suit against his brother. He would have been farther ahead if he had not done so. He lost the initial suit in the local circuit court, and appealed to the Michigan State Supreme Court. The justices decided that it was W. K.'s company which had made the trade name "Kellogg's" valuable. He alone had a right to attach it to any food products. A quarter of a million dollars poorer as the result of his quarrels, John Harvey decided to call it quits. He changed his company's name to the Battle Creek Food Company, continuing to market breakfast cereals, digestive aids, health candies, and vegetarian proteins until his death in 1943.

W. K. saw no reason why he should not shorten the name of the Kellogg Toasted Corn Flake Company to the Kellogg Company. As he broadened his line of prepared breakfast foods, he continued the aggressive merchandising techniques which had proved so successful with corn flakes. Even during the Great Depression, when most manufacturers were cutting back, Will Kellogg ordered the advertising budget increased. Again, he guessed right; the company's sales figures never faltered in their upward march.

What of C. W. Post, the genius who first discerned that "health" foods manufactured for people with troubled stomachs could be marketed as convenience foods for the whole gamut of Americans—well, sick, and those afraid of getting sick? In 1914, the chronic stomach problems which had plagued Post for years necessitated a hurried trip to the Mayo Brothers' Clinic for surgery. Afterwards, he returned to his Santa Barbara, California, home feeling somewhat better. But his spells of melancholia persisted. One morning, he killed himself with a 30-30 hunting rifle, the only one of his firearms collection which had not been packed away out of sight and reach. He had not quite reached his sixtieth birthday.

John Harvey Kellogg kept active as surgeon, author, food manufacturer, and health propagandist until his final bout with pneumonia just two months short of his ninety-second year. As for Will, he was determined to beat his elder brother once more by living longer. He came three months short of making good on his attempt.

Three men, vastly different in personality, talents, and motivation, had greatly modified America's eating habits—yes, and eventually those of millions more in many countries of the world.

If Mr. Post were to be dropped from an airship on a desert island in uncharted seas, he would begin at once to take note of the things about him that were of utility.

If the island were inhabited, C. W. Post would proceed to round up the natives and teach them to use his special brand of coconuts. Inside of three weeks he'd have them fighting for him and organizing to repel all invaders. In six months the natives would have adopted fig leaves . . . "grown only on Post trees". . . and inside of a year he'd be mayor of the island and king of the Lulaloos.

Later on he would introduce shoes and sandals made from "Post cocoa bark," and when the rescue party finally found him he'd be in a position to buy the ship and sail it home as master.—Zach Moore, journalist, 1909.

The great Battle Creek cereal boom as the cartoonists saw it.

"Historic moments in the annals of American Industry— An efficiency engineer discovers that printing will save Mr. Kellogg from having to sign his name on each of the Corn Flakes boxes."—Drawing by Rea Irvin; Copr. 1936, 1964 The New Yorker Magazine, Inc.

Granola, Postum, Corn Flakes, and Peanut Butter

Over forty cereal companies were formed in Calhoun County, Michigan, in the years 1902-1906, but Only Post and Kellogg survived. This cartoon by James T. McCutcheon is from the Chicago Tribune.

W. K. KELLOGG, A
BLAZED NEW
MARKETING AN

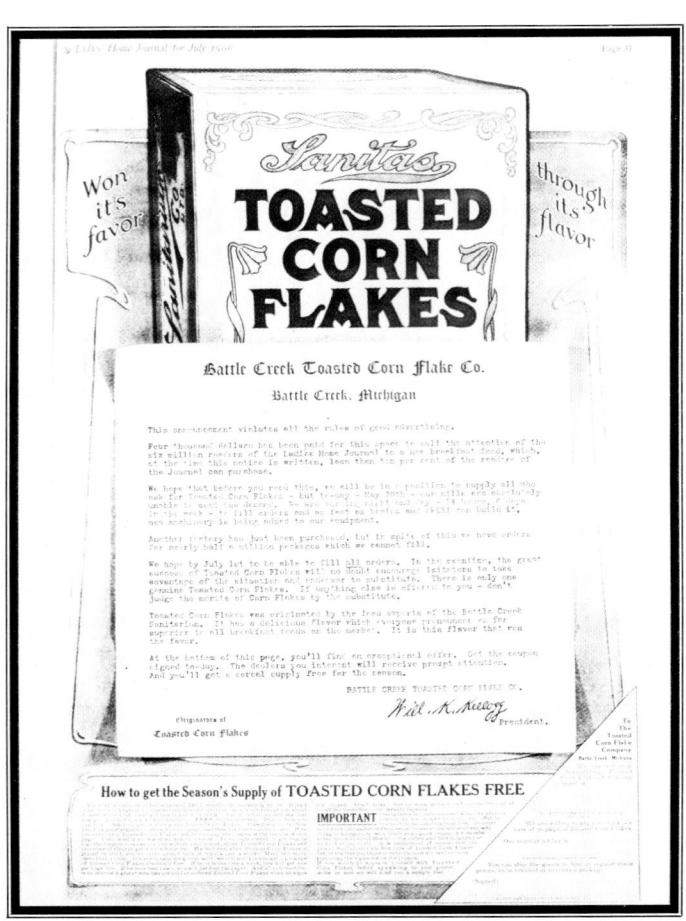

Kellogg's first advertisement proclaimed, "This announcement violates all the rules of good advertising." Actually it didn't; people paid attention.

AGGRESSIVE PROMOTER, TRAILS IN ADVERTISING

WILL KEITH MADE GOOD USE OF ANOTHER MICHIGAN PRODUCT —THE AUTOMOBILE— IN PROMOTING AND SELLING HIS CEREALS

EEK, ESTABLISHED 1906

Kellogg's cereals became as much a part of the American grocery store as the cracker barrel. Kids recruited to give away sample cereal packages helped put Corn Flakes, Pep, Bran, other cereals on American breakfast tables.

Drs. Mary and David Paulson
"As a spiritual force and as a reformatory force in the world, if we fall down on that it would be better if we had never been born."

THAT'S A WONDERFUL BARGAIN, BUT WE HAVEN'T A CENT

"WHERE'S YOUR FAITH?"
DEMANDS
DAVID PAULSON,
APOSTLE
TO
CHICAGO

avid and Mary Paulson liked the property, the former home of Judge Beckwith of Chicago. It had broad lawns, trees, and a brook; and east of the estate lay a sixteen-acre wooded area. The place had lain unoccupied for the past seven years. Dr. David reviewed the requirements: "Patients should have fresh air, sunshine, exercise, pure water, rest, a wholesome diet, a beautiful outlook, peace of mind—"

"The place is ideal," he decided, "but what is the price?"

"Sixteen thousand dollars."

"That's a wonderful bargain," said Mary, "but we haven't a cent."

David's response, a typical Paulsonism, was, "Where's your faith?"

David Paulson's manner of plunging into a major business transaction would have horrified any auditor—and excited admiration in Monte Carlo—except, of course, that the devout doctor saw no gamble, no possibility of failure in any enterprise the Lord wanted him to attempt.

The devout man believed every verse in the Bible except Luke 14:28: "For which of you, intending to build a tower, sitteth not down first, and counteth the cost, whether he have sufficient to finish it." In his memoirs, appropriately called *Footprints of Faith*, he revealed his reasoning:

"We did not have any money; and we knew no one to whom we could look for any. But we felt impressed it was the thing to do so we moved out here March 4, 1904. . . .

"We did not move out here for our health. I had to borrow money to ship our goods out, but I had the sweet conviction in my soul that I was launching out in obedience to a divine providence and I have not any doubt that I will live to see it done.

"We moved into a little house on the grounds —the tramps had carried away the doors—and came out here to start a sanitarium. It was a great joke to my friends. . . . They said, 'There is Dr. Paulson moving out to a rich residence town to start a sanitarium without money enough to take his bed along.' They had infallible proof that I was a lunatic."

Even the saintly Dr. Paulson could not resist saying "I told you so" later; "The institution is here. Why? I knew God wanted this sort of thing near Chicago. . . . By the way, several of those same friends have been around here since and wanted jobs."

Just who was this extraordinary Dr. Paulson, and where did he come from?

A six-foot orphan farm boy from a sod house in South Dakota, expressing himself in torrents of Danish-American speech, appeared at Battle Creek College in the fall of 1888. His lanky arms dangled out of the too-short sleeves of his home-

95

spun coat, and his skimpy trouser legs displayed several inches of shinbone. He brought with him almost enough money to make it through the year, and enough determination to make it through a lifetime. His money came from personal savings and those of his older brother Nels. The determination he showed is one of those eternal mysteries. He had it at an early age, and it never left him. It gave him the courage to attempt the near impossible and overcome it. He had had so little schooling in South Dakota that, as he later confessed, "I could not have told the difference between a verb and a noun if I had met them on the street." Yet, two years after his arrival in Battle Creek he had finished his premedical course.

During those two years, he worked at Kellogg's Sanitarium five hours a day and more in the summer, cleaning rooms, washing windows, beating carpets, delivering hot water to patients' rooms, running errands. *Running* them. He wouldn't slow down. The other boys said, "Paulson likes to work, let him do it." When Mrs. Hall, the matron, left the room, the boys, except Paulson, would relax. "I'm working for the Lord," he explained.

"You act like you're the manager," one of the boys derided.

"I feel like one," Paulson retorted.

This young man in a hurry managed to work and study at the same time. He usually carried a book with him and read a few lines while riding the elevators; then he concentrated on what he had read until he could snatch another look at the book. He learned a great deal this way, and also acquired notoriety for his absentmindedness.

He walked fast, read fast, talked so fast some people couldn't understand him. When other students asked him how he got his lessons while working so many hours a day, he facetiously replied, "Take your textbook to bed with you and sleep with it under your pillow."

In those years Adventist aspirants to the medical degree usually attended the University of Michigan Medical College at Ann Arbor for three years, completing their fourth year at Northwestern University in Illinois, or at Bellevue in New York City. David chose the latter; Mary Wild, the future Dr. Mary Paulson, two years behind him, attended Northwestern.

For David, the year in New York not only provided him with the best medical instruction available, but also gave him an intimate view of the needs of a large class of American poor.

When he returned to Battle Creek in 1894 as a staff member in the famous Sanitarium, he was prepared to join enthusiastically with Dr. J. H. Kellogg in rescue-mission work in Battle Creek and Chicago.

While David was studying at Ann Arbor, two of the Wessels brothers, who had made a fortune in the diamond mines of Kimberley, South Africa, had given Dr. Kellogg $40,000 to start a medical mission in Chicago. By the time Paulson graduated, several mission projects were in progress in Chicago, including a sanitarium in the south side. An amazing number of people needed help: unwed mothers, prostitutes, runaways, drunks, derelicts of all kinds, besides the expected poor and ignorant—all needing medical care and the uplifting influence Christians could give.

A year later the American Medical Missionary College was initiated, using campuses in Battle Creek and Chicago. Paulson instructed on both campuses. In 1896, Mary Wild completed her medical studies, graduated, and married Dr. Paulson. The couple spent a three-week honeymoon in New York in postgraduate study. From then on, it was Doctors David and Mary, who, after a short time spent in directing the Battle Creek Sanitarium in Dr. Kellogg's absence, went to 1926 Wabash Avenue, Chicago, for a four-year term of supervision of the entire medical-mission project in that city.

Paulson wanted to save all the poor people of Chicago, spiritually and physically. In attempting to do so he acquired an exhaustless supply of stories showing God's power to save anyone. He wrote, "Our cities are a perfect cesspool. They are the place into which everything drains. I was never before so much impressed with the absolute necessity of the gospel to break the bondage of sin as when seeking the lost jewels amid all the moral rubbish found in Chicago in those early days, and on the other hand I learned as never before and saw it illustrated by many shining examples that whomsoever the Son sets free is free indeed.

"I remember an Irishman who was converted at the Life Boat mission. He prayed and struggled to be delivered from booze, but said his civilization broke down whenever he passed a saloon. He was finally delivered from his appetite and the Lord set him free."

In 1903, Paulson was invited to visit Europe for three months. With the great needs of Chicago heavy on his mind, the young doctor

"That's a Wonderful Bargain, But We Haven't a Cent"

Prayer meeting at the old Chicago Mission.

visited the noted Dr. Barnardo of London. Here was a Christian man of thirty-four who had spent $15,000,000 of unsolicited gift money in rescuing 50,000 children from lives of crime, with only three percent failure. Paulson reported on his trip: "I felt in my bones that when I would come back I should be able to accomplish more for Chicago. If I had had any other view, nothing else,—no board or committee on earth, could have made me believe that I should leave it for a single night. I had always wanted to go to Europe, but . . . my attachment for the work in sin-cursed Chicago far overwhelmed it."

David Paulson was already a man of faith and prayer. Dr. Barnardo had demonstrated what such a life could accomplish. Upon his return to Chicago, Dr. Paulson began to look for a place to establish a large representative sanitarium. Here the story of Hinsdale really starts.

First, a problem needed attention. The Chicago Life Boat Home for Girls was surrounded by saloons and brothels on South Clark Street. The Home needed a new location. One of Dr. Paulson's patients, Mr. C. B. Kimbell, a wealthy Chicago businessman who knew of Dr. Paulson's mission problems, suggested that he establish the Home for Girls in a two-story dwelling he owned in West Hinsdale, the rent to be free for the first six months, a small fee to be charged thereafter. The home made the move.

Hinsdale was a prosperous residential community seventeen miles west of Chicago. Mr. Kimbell lived there and owned several properties. It was quite natural for him to suggest Hinsdale as a good location for Dr. Paulson's new sanitarium. He asked Dr. Paulson to look at a ten-acre estate with a fifteen-room house, a nine-room house, and outbuildings, and to worry about the price later. The price, it turned out, was $16,000

It was then that Dr. Mary exclaimed, "That's a wonderful bargain, but we haven't a cent"; and David admonished, "Where's your faith?"

The Paulsons returned to Chicago and called a meeting of the "family." The workers heard the report about the Hinsdale opportunity; then they prayed enthusiastically for the fulfillment of their hopes. A way appeared a few days later when Mr. Kimbell offered to buy the property, deed it to the American Medical Missionary College, and look for reimbursement in twenty yearly payments without interest.

There was much work to be done on the buildings and grounds. A man who was only an acquaintance donated $200 to help with the rehabilitation. Later, a woman came forward with a $2,500 loan. The Beckwith home, moved a hundred feet to the west, became the main sanitarium facility. Other buildings were altered to serve as dormitory, workers' home, and

Drs. David and Mary Paulson, surrounded by Battle Creek Sanitarium nurses and other personnel. Dr. David was an instructor in the American Medical Missionary College in both Battle Creek and Chicago; he had charge of the entire institution during one of Dr. Kellogg's trips to Europe. Then the dedicated couple moved to Chicago to run the medical mission work in that city.

maintenance shops. In the fall of 1904, the emerging institution was deeded to the Hinsdale Sanitarium and Benevolent Association, a nonprofit organization governed by a board of directors, of which Mr. Kimbell was president. Mr. Kimbell agreed to finance a new building, at a cost of $100,000, to replace the original Beckwith home. The charter of the new association provided not only for a patient-care facility but also for a training school for nurses and other medical missionaries. Familiar names on the roster of the board were the Drs. David and Mary Paulson; Nels Paulson, David's older brother; L. H. Christian; and John Harvey Kellogg. Additional properties were acquired in the following months.

Patients began to arrive, filling all available space. More money came in—$1,150 from a man in Kansas who had sold a farm; $5,000 from a former patient at Battle Creek. On February 18, 1905, Mr. Kimbell died, and Dr. Paulson replaced him as president of the board. In lieu of Mr. Kimbell's gift building, the Beckwith house was enlarged.

Late in 1906, as the enlargement neared completion, many patients clamored for admission. The new building was sorely needed. An unusual incident explains the means by which this building became a reality.

Mr. H. E. Hoyt, secretary-treasurer of the Benevolent Association, journeyed to Wisconsin to visit a former donor, Mrs. Van Houten, hoping to get some help for pressing needs. At first, he was spurned from the door, Mrs. Van Houten explaining that her husband was drunk and did not want callers. His drinking habits, she said, were of long standing and incorrigible. Finally invited to enter, Hoyt managed to get the man's attention, and before long they were on their knees praying for help. The result was the complete reformation of Mr. Van Houten and a new life for the couple. Hoyt left without a donation but with satisfaction in the blessing he had brought to the home.

Nine months later Mrs. Van Houten wrote, appealing for help for her husband, still sober but facing a difficulty in settling the estate of his deceased brother in New York City. Hoyt and Paulson at once went to New York, arriving just in time to save Van Houten from signing

away the estate to an unscrupulous lawyer. The Van Houtens at once willed their own possessions and the brother's estate to the Hinsdale Sanitarium. Within a few months, Mr. Van Houten died, still a Christian. Mrs. Van Houten provided the needed money for the "old sanitarium" building facing North Oak Street, where the Beckwith house originally stood.

During the construction of the new building, Dr. Paulson's attention was called to the severe overcrowding in the Life Boat Rescue Home located in the small Hinsdale dwelling house provided by Mr. Kimbell. The matron had accumulated a fund of $1,000, which Dr. Paulson at once used to buy a lot four and one-half blocks from the sanitarium. From many sources, money came in to complete the new home for girls, a four-story structure with thirty rooms, paid for by 1909. A branch of this home was opened in the little southside sanitarium in Chicago, which had been idle for some time.

In 1910, a building west of the expanded Beckwith home was remodeled to form the Good Samaritan Inn, later called Elmwood Hall, where

Above: Life Boat *advised boys to turn their backs on tobacco, and showed them exactly how to do it.*

Left: Dr. Paulson's Life Boat *magazine economized by using the same cover picture year after year.*

the poor could receive simple medical care at a price within their reach.

During the years of concentration on the Hinsdale Sanitarium, which catered to a relatively affluent clientele, Dr. Paulson's abiding interest in the poor had to be somewhat slighted, though every year thousands of dollars' worth of services at the sanitarium were devoted to charity. Now he administered, in addition to the sanitarium with its schools of nursing, the Good Samaritan Inn and Girls' Home with its Chicago branch.

The Chicago medical mission had begun to decline following the 1902 fire at the Battle Creek Sanitarium. In 1910 the American Medical Missionary College gave place to the new College of Medical Evangelists in Loma Linda, California. Another factor which worked to diminish the mission endeavor in Chicago was the counsel of Ellen G. White that Seventh-day Adventist denominational resources should be used more for evangelistic enterprises, less for the nondenominational welfare endeavors that had been urged by Dr. Kellogg. It was also true that other agencies were ministering to the poor of Chicago.

The sanitarium prospered. In time, occupational therapy was introduced, and a secondary school was developed for instruction of young workers.

Dr. David was paid $40 a week. Dr. Mary was offered $75 a month, but accepted only $65.

In 1914 Dr. David's health began to fail, and he sought relief in more healthful climates. It was a losing struggle. At the last, a raging fever resisted all methods of cure. He asked to be taken to Asheville, North Carolina. His friend Dr. Percy T. Magan came to stay with him. But the end was near. W. K. Kellogg, the cereal king, came 2,000 miles, arriving an hour before David Paulson's death on October 15, 1916. W. K. insisted on paying all funeral expenses. Kellogg said, "Dr. Paulson has done more for me than any man on earth. What little I can do now is nothing."

Paulson was only 48 years old. Twenty-eight years had elapsed since he appeared at Battle Creek College to prepare for a medical career, twelve years since the founding of Hinsdale Sanitarium. He had lived a full life in those short years.

He was a dynamic leader with charisma, depending upon faith for the fulfillment of his practical, wholly selfless ambitions, and of his urge to heal. His prayers brought many a patient through critical illness, sometimes saved them from almost certain death. He was a great personality, who left his influence on all with whom he worked. One could often identify workers

An advertisement in Life Boat *featured an open air tent for sleeping out-of-doors while indoors.*

from those early years at Hinsdale by hearing them repeat, "As Dr. Paulson used to say—"

What *did* Dr. Paulson say? Here are examples:

"I learned as a personal experience that if a man bows before his Creator, he never needs to bow before his fellowmen. The Lord will see to it that he has standing room."

"As a physician, I desire to see people delivered from headache, intercostal neuralgia, gastric ulcers, neuritis, rheumatism, and all those other physical torments. But I ten times more desire to see them cured of their sins. If I did not, I might better be a horse doctor. . . . To be saved from sin is the most important experience that could possibly come to us in this life."

"There is no more sense in your clinging to pet sins because other people do than there would be in your keeping bedbugs in your bedroom because you knew some of your neighbors who had them."

"Once a man had fallen through the ice, and some people were trying to help him out by thrusting a plank at him. It soon became icy so that each time he tried to take hold of it his hand slipped off. Finally, he gasped, 'For God's sake give me the warm end of the plank!' And when they thrust him the other end of the plank his hands clung to it and his life was saved. Perhaps you and I are constantly holding out to people the frozen end of the plank."

"In the Battle Creek Sanitarium there was a good deal of backsliding. It wrung my soul. The thought came to me that I must pray more in secret. I thought of the fresh-air shaft leading out from the basement, where no one ever visited. I went there to pray several times a day. That place saved my soul. I need it just as much today."

Of Chicago: "There are jewels hidden in all this moral rubbish."

"To love a dirty, rough street urchin whose hair was full of vermin—how could I do it? I asked God to put His love in my heart for them, and He answered my prayer, and then I found it unnecessary to advertise the fact to them. The language of love is universal."

If Paulson's lifelong pouring forth of advice, aphorisms, and preachments sounds oppressive, remember that with Paulson there was a major difference: He lived what he preached. He stressed prayer, and he prayed much. He urged others to have faith; he exercised it himself constantly. He preached compassion, and he poured out his life in sympathetic concern for those who needed help most.

As he had confessed, "I asked God to put His love in my heart." That was one prayer out of many that God answered in all abundance.

"This boy is four and one-half years old. He was the first baby born in our home. His mother is now married to a good Christian man, and they have a happy Christian home."

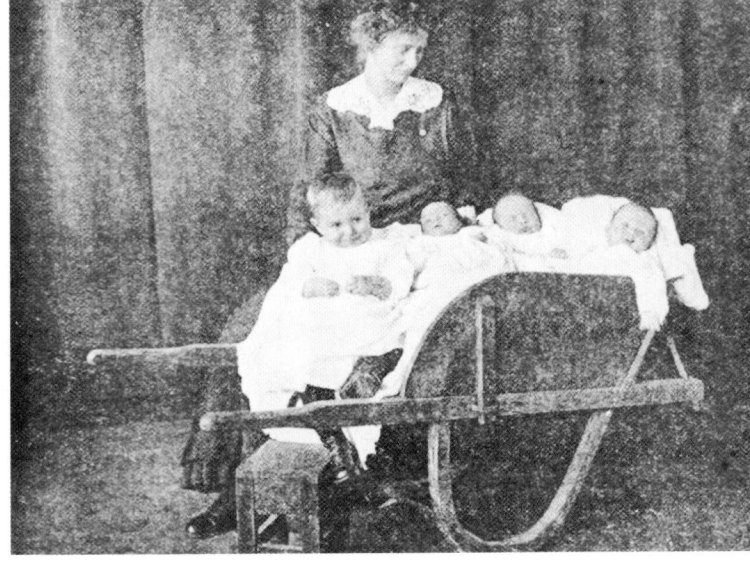

"Miss Sanborn and her wheelbarrow load of babies."

DAVID
PA
SPECIALIZED
FOR ORPHA

"Bessie and her little brother Norman who are being cared for temporarily at the Good Samaritan Inn and the Home respectively."

"One of our promising Home boys."

"Is it worth our while to have tried to give these little innocent tots who are worse than fatherless a right start in life?"

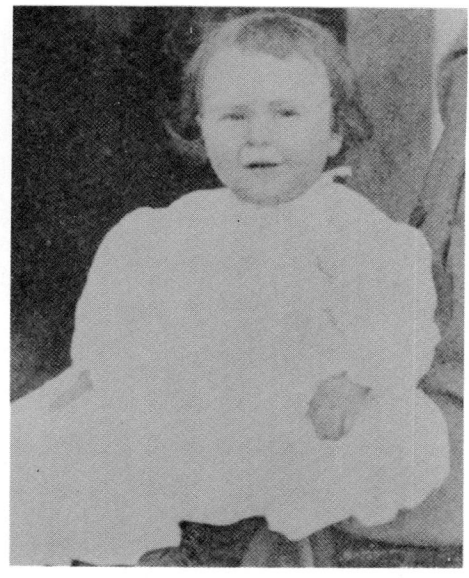

"Baby Emmel, born in our Home sixteen months ago, is being tenderly cared for by his own mother."

D MARY
SON
INDING HOMES
AND WAIFS

"A group of street children who were anxious to have their pictures taken."

"This beautiful child was found in a Chicago garbage can when a mere babe, and was sent to our Home. He was a bright sunbeam while with us and is now the joy and delight of a good Christian home."

The Vision Bold

The Beckwith house, the original Hinsdale Sanitarium building.

An early game of tennis at Hinsdale.

Hinsdale Sanitarium as it appeared before modern brick additions were built.

Dr. Mary Paulson in 1923, seven years after her husband's death.

Dr. J. F. Morse, a member of the Hinsdale medical staff in the 1920's.

WESTWARD

ANOTHER KELLOGG, ANOTHER SAN

"WATER VAPORS,
HOT AIR, AND ELECTRIC BATHS"
COME
TO
SAINT HELENA

I wish to state to the public that I shall immediately commence to erect buildings suitable to treat patients on the hygienic system. . . . They will be located two and a half miles from Saint Helena. The location is all that could be desired. The buildings will be two hundred and fifty feet above the valley. This elevation is covered with the most beautiful natural groves of pine, fir, redwood and manzanita, bay and madrone. . . . A mountain spring of pure, soft water one hundred feet above the buildings will give a liberal supply for all purposes. The climate, location, and surroundings are not second to any other locality in California for the recovery and preservation of health."

Thus wrote Merritt G. Kellogg in *Signs of the Times,* November 22, 1877.

Merritt, eldest son of John P. Kellogg of Battle Creek, Michigan, deserves a prominent place in the annals of Adventist pioneers. That he is not better known is the natural result of a Kellogg family matter. Of seventeen children born to Merritt's father, two became world-famous— John Harvey of Battle Creek Sanitarium, and Will Keith, the corn-flake man. With two half-brothers like that, small wonder that Merritt's name has fallen into near eclipse.

Probably, Merritt Kellogg never wasted a precious minute worrying that his prominent relatives had preempted the name Kellogg. Merritt was hewn from the same quality granite as the doughtiest of the pioneers. The first Seventh-day Adventist ever to set foot in California or anywhere on the west coast, he was dedicated, resourceful, and energetic. He was a co-owner with Ellen White, John Loughborough, and others of that soaring faith which enabled them to see splendid visions, then set about turning those dreams into concrete accomplishments.

Accepting the Adventist faith in Battle Creek at the age of twenty, he became the first superintendent of the Battle Creek Sabbath School. In 1859, he migrated with his family to California by oxcart, settling in the rough, tough town of San Francisco, where he supported his family working as a carpenter. He set to work promptly studying the Bible with those who listen. Two years after his arrival, he held evangelistic meetings and baptized fourteen converts.

He earned good wages in San Francisco, but he felt he was not doing what God had designed for him. Accordingly, he sold his home, left his business, and returned east, enrolling in Dr. Trall's Hygieo-Therapeutic College in New Jersey. Six months later, he emerged a physician.

In a letter to Ellen White, he wrote, "I did this because I believed the work of health reform was of God and that God had a work for me to do in the message."

Elder and Mrs. White, from their own previous experiences, feared that Kellogg might have picked up some erroneous ideas from Dr. Trall— ideas "objectionable, either in theory or in zeal to carry some points to extreme." But after talking with the newly graduated physician, James

White wrote in the *Review and Herald* that he was "happily disappointed." On the contrary, "the harmony between what the Lord has revealed relative to this subject, and science, has been a theme of most interesting conversation, and mutual profit."

Kellogg gave some health lectures in the churches in Michigan which further allayed Elder White's fears. After listening to one of the doctor's lectures, White wrote for *Review* readers, "Our ministers speak on the subject of health from a Bible standpoint. This seems right. Brother Kellogg treats the subject from a scientific view, and we think well calculated to teach the people and lead them to a practical understanding of how to live."

His medical preparation behind him, Dr. Kellogg attended the 1868 General Conference session in Battle Creek, where he pleaded for some leading ministers to visit golden California where, he was confident, golden opportunities awaited them in evangelism.

John Loughborough and D. T. Bourdeau felt impressed to answer the invitation. They left for California, sailing on the *Rising Star* through the Caribbean to Aspinwall, crossing the Panama Isthmus by train, then taking another sailing ship, the *Golden City*, up the Pacific Coast to San Francisco.

"There were not then a dozen professed Seventh-day Adventists in this whole Pacific slope," Loughborough later wrote. Since Kellogg had baptized fourteen, perhaps several had died, lost heart, or moved away. Or perhaps Loughborough was rounding the number to the nearest dozen. At any rate, the two preachers looked for a free vacant lot upon which to pitch their new $1,000 evangelistic tent. But no one would donate the use of a lot, so the ministers accepted an invitation to preach in Petaluma, a town thirty miles to the north.

Dr. Merritt Kellogg joined the evangelists in their meetings, speaking on health subjects. In 1870, Loughborough and Kellogg were preaching in the hamlet of Bloomfield, southwest of Santa Rosa, when an epidemic of smallpox broke out. They closed their meetings and went to work treating the sick. A local physician using drugs lost four patients out of five, while Kellogg and Loughborough saved ten out of eleven using water treatments and healthful diet. As a result, Kellogg's fame as a physician spread. All of this happened three years *before* Merritt's precocious kid brother John Harvey Kellogg—the famous Dr. Kellogg—enrolled in his medical course at Bellevue.

Thanks largely to the influence of this minister-doctor cooperation, Adventist membership in California grew to 130 by 1871, 320 in 1873, and the next year 500, out of 7,500 in the entire denomination. This was 1874, the year of the founding of Battle Creek College; the sailing of John N. Andrews, the first Adventist foreign missionary, for Switzerland; and, in Oakland, the first issues of *Signs of the Times*. The Western Health Reform Institute had been operating in Battle Creek, Michigan, for eight years. Elder Loughborough, with a series of assistants, was holding public meetings.

After helping Loughborough with his meetings in several towns, Merritt Kellogg settled near the village of Rutherford, four miles south of Saint Helena, in the heart of the Napa Valley wine-grape country.

In Saint Helena, a group of Adventist believers had been organized, including Mr. William A. Pratt, a retired bricklayer who owned a large acreage northeast of town, and Mr. A. B. Atwood, a new convert. These two men would join Dr. Kellogg in making an important commitment.

At the camp meeting of 1874 in Yountville, nine miles south of Saint Helena, there had been talk of starting a health institute. Elder J. N. Loughborough, president of the new California Conference, had previously helped in the founding of the Battle Creek institution, and he was now eager to start such a project in California. After camp meeting, Elder Loughborough and Elder I. D. Van Horn were in Saint Helena planning for the construction of a meeting house. Van Horn did some exploring in the hill area northeast of town and discovered an "ideal place for a health resort"—Crystal Springs, two and a half miles away. Mr. Pratt owned the spring and surrounding acreage.

In the summer of 1877, Mr. Atwood took his wife to Rutherford for medical treatment by Dr. Kellogg, whose need for better medical facilities was obvious. The result was that Atwood talked to his friend Pratt, and the three men took action. Pratt furnished ten acres of land, an interest in the spring, and $3,000; Atwood furnished $1,000; and Kellogg promised $1,000 in labor.

Building and road making began at once. Local clay was used to make brick for the foundation. James and Ellen White, who had come west for an extended stay, journeyed from Oakland to view the project. Ellen remarked that she had seen the road and surroundings in vision. A stock company was formed, establishing the "Rural Health Retreat Association" with Pratt as president, Atwood as treasurer, Kellogg as manager. The trustees met first on February 15, 1878.

An early stockholder was John Morrison of Santa Rosa, who received $200 worth of stock in payment for a team of horses to be used for hauling lumber. Morrison, father-in-law of Elder William Healey, had already joined James White in buying Oakland property for the Pacific Press building of 1875.

The first building of the health retreat was a two-story structure, 72 x 28 feet, with a thirteen-bed capacity. Named The Rural Health Retreat, it opened on June 7, 1878, with seven guests. Soon the employees had to move into tents. The hillside behind the building was excavated and an addition was constructed for the 1879 patronage.

The "Retreat" ran the following ad in a local newspaper:

"A pleasant summer resort, where invalids are cared for hygienically, . . . where those who have tried the drug system of medicine without benefit are cured by Nature's own remedies. All the various forms of water vapors, hot air, medicated and electric baths, Swedish movements, proper exercise and rest. Pure soft water and wholesome diet. Agreeable mental influences, delightful climate, beautiful scenery, and pleasant surroundings. Medications such as each individual case may demand. . . .

"The buildings are new and newly furnished, and are located in the most healthful climate and surrounded by the most beautiful scenery in California.

"The Institute is situated four hundred feet above Napa Valley, which it immediately overlooks."

Dr. Kellogg was not bragging—just telling the truth about the loveliness of this corner of Eden, and the many advantages to prospective patients of visiting the same. Who could blame him?

Late in 1879, Dr. Kellogg moved to Los Angeles, leaving "the retreat" without a doctor for one year, during which it operated as the health resort. Then Dr. Ellet J. Waggoner, who had received his training at Bellevue Medical College and at Battle Creek under Dr. Kellogg, with the

Dr. and Mrs. Merritt G. Kellogg, Seventh-day Adventist pioneers on the West Coast. Dr. Kellogg was a co-founder of Rural Health Retreat.

William A. Pratt, who gave ten acres, an interest in a spring, and $3,000 to build the Rural Health Retreat near the town of Saint Helena.

Main Street, Saint Helena, California.

help of other physicians filled the gap for a few years. Dr. Waggoner later achieved prominence as editor of *Signs of the Times* and protagonist of righteousness by faith at the 1888 General Conference Session in Minneapolis.

The operation had its ups and downs. In 1884, Mr. Pratt, wishing to surround the fledgling institution with an Adventist community which he felt would bring strength to the project, offered to give to his friends free land south of the institution at a half-acre per family if they would move to the community and build a home. When several accepted, Pratt approached Ellen White, now a widow living in Healdsburg, confident that her presence would be an asset to the institution. She replied that she wished to buy ten acres just south of the institution. Pratt protested that it would spoil his plan, to which Mrs. White replied, "That is exactly what I want to do. Someday," she said, "you will need this land and I want to hold it till you are ready to buy it for the retreat."

Pratt thought it over and reluctantly consented, selling Ellen White the eight and a half acres which could be used for buildings. On this land not far from the Sanitarium buildings, she erected a three-story home planned for institutional use, which, when needed, was made available to the sanitarium. She resisted giving a friend the particular choice building site on the brow of the hill on the basis that "there will be other buildings here some day." Her foresight was justified twenty-three years later when in 1907 on that precise spot the four-story hospital building was built and put in operation. Not only did the growing sanitarium need all the acreage held for some years by Ellen White, but also other adjacent properties.

From 1879 to 1888, the institution made progress under the management of J. D. Rice, who improved the buildings and the equipment. In 1885, Dr. J. S. Gibbs from Battle Creek became medical superintendent. A year later, Dr. W. P. Burke joined him. After a year of feuding, Dr. Burke left to set up a rival and damaging practice in Napa twenty miles south.

In 1891, a nursing school was begun, one of the first in the West. Its graduates were in big demand.

In 1885, Elder J. H. Waggoner, editor of *Signs of the Times*, was chosen also to edit a new publication, the *Pacific Health Journal*, a joint project of the Pacific Press and the Rural Health Retreat.

During the 1890's, the retreat was renamed Saint Helena Sanitarium. Ellen White kept in close touch with the institution and led in counsel and shaping policies. Pointed issues were natural methods of therapy as opposed to drug therapy, vegetarian versus flesh diets, and the

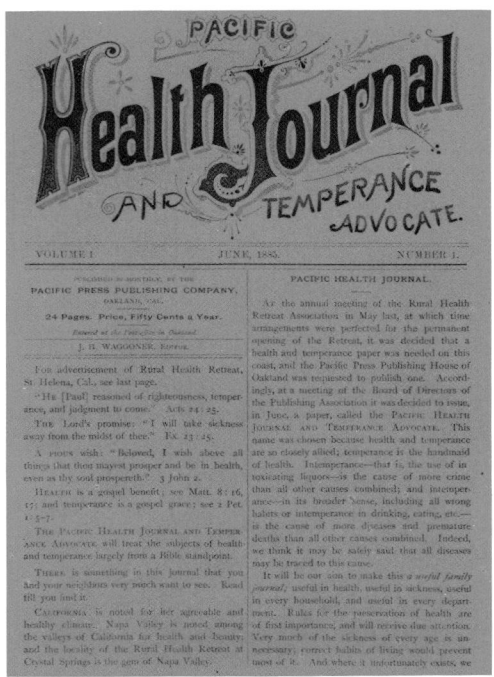

In 1891, John A. Burden was chosen business manager. Adventist trained, only twenty-nine years old at the time, Burden had implicit confidence in the Lord's leading through Ellen White. He was to play a key role in the developing sanitarium and health food work in California and Australia.

The young manager followed developments with keen interest as the Kellogg brothers of Battle Creek forged ahead in the development of health foods. He felt sure that such an industry would also succeed in California. In 1898, in a tiny building just to the north of the sanitarium, Burden opened health food manufacture by putting two ovens and two men, a baker and an assistant, to work making whole-wheat bread. The business grew so rapidly that a factory building was soon called for.

Since the crowded ledge on Howell Mountain provided no room for a factory, in 1900 Burden purchased eighty-five acres of hill and valley land of the adjoining Robert Pratt property. Thus in one move he obtained the Pratt half of Crystal Spring, doubling the sanitarium's water supply; he acquired land for the health food factory; and he secured ten acres at the far end for sewage disposal. Burden closed the deal on his own responsibility, little realizing that within a few months he would sell to Ellen G. White the well-built home and sixty-five acres of land—Elmshaven—which neither he nor the sanitarium needed.

The new four-story food factory opened in early 1901. The machinery included "two large reel ovens, five granose flake machines, a granose mill," and equipment "for making unfermented grape juice." It was "a thoroughly up-to-date factory" with thirty-two employees, according to an account in *Pacific Union Recorder*.

Besides good bread, the factory turned out

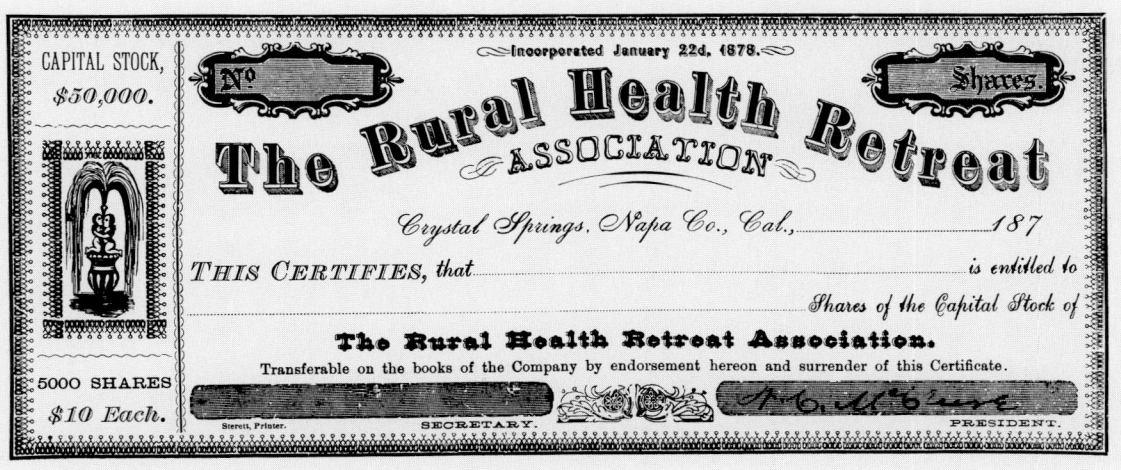

The Rural Health Retreat stock certificate created momentary consternation. Without authorization the printer had embellished the paper with a picture of a fountain upon which two human figures, in a state of dishabille, embraced each other.

Dr. Merritt Kellogg wrote the minutes of the organizational meetings for the Rural Health Retreat Association.

granose flakes and biscuits, crackers, cereal coffee, peanut butter, malted nuts, grape juice, and finally, Nut Cero and Nut Loaf, meat substitutes. Sales reached out to "every city and town in California." The sanitarium put health food stores in operation in leading cities in northern California. Early plans called for a business in dried fruits and the shipping of health foods to the Pacific islands. Competition was minimal and business was good. A night shift worked to keep up with orders.

In 1901, Burden was called to Australia to engage in sanitarium and health food work, and did not return to America until 1904. The Saint Helena food business operated for about twenty years, but without Burden's vision and skilled management it eventually closed.

Mrs. White kept before the Saint Helena Sanitarium its purpose of supporting the objectives of the Adventist church and of resisting the influence of the Battle Creek Sanitarium toward becoming nondenominational. Upon her return from Australia in 1900, she lived at Elmshaven, the home she purchased from Burden, just down the hill from the sanitarium. Here she resided till her death in 1915.

And what of Dr. Merritt Kellogg? He sailed in 1893 on the ship *Pitcairn* for medical missionary work in the South Seas. He served in Tonga, then sailed to Australia where he drew plans for the Sydney Sanitarium and helped build it. Returning to America in 1903, he made his home in Healdsburg, California, until he died in 1922.

The sanitarium he helped start in Saint Helena has grown through many stages into today's 108-bed hospital combined with a health center with 42 rooms. It includes a building called Oakhurst with 24 rooms for long-term

Rural Health Retreat "bath folks" in 1892. Left to right: Unidentified, Lena Talyer, Annie King, Florence Butz, Algie Cook.

Nurses in "bath room" uniform in 1895.

guests, and Crystal Springs Manor, a retirement residence.

The Saint Helena Hospital and Health Center is one of only a few such institutions which has preserved its rural atmosphere. Howell Mountain remains a wilderness area. Even today, tall pines and firs grace the hills on all sides, isolating the hospital from the vineyards and towns of Napa Valley and from the San Francisco Bay cities farther south.

The "health retreat" idea still survives. Guests come to escape the pollution and pressures of modern life, to rest, eat wholesome food, enjoy contact with nature, receive invigorating treatments, and reorient their lives. With renewed emphasis on the cure of the whole person, Saint Helena Hospital and Health Center strives to be worthy of the name its founders gave it almost a century ago—Rural Health Retreat.

The Vision Bold

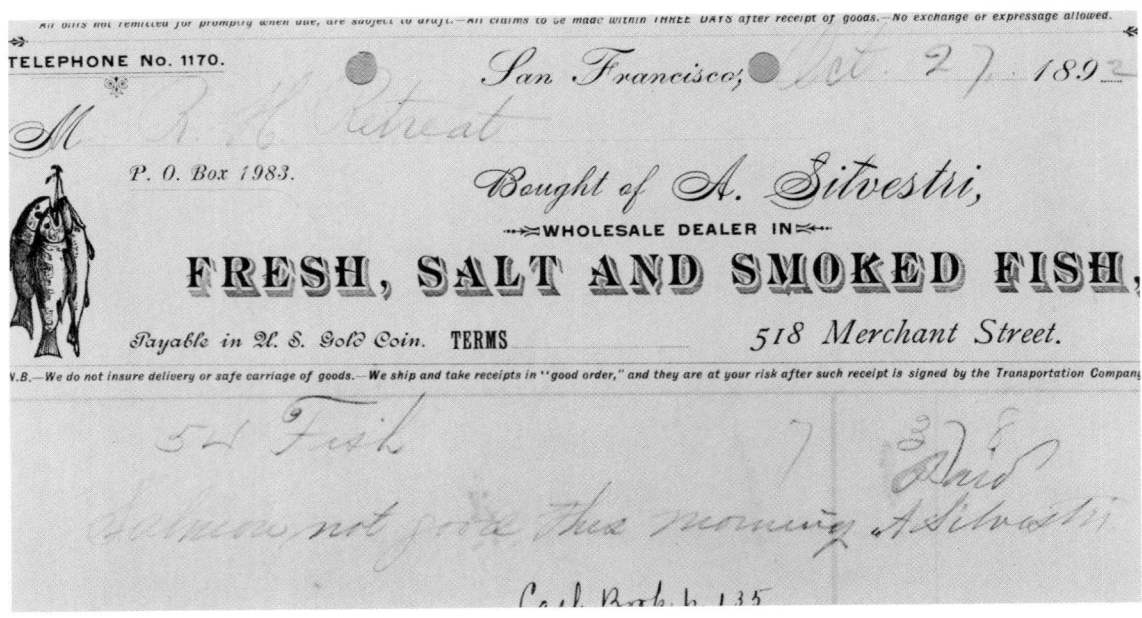

Some nonvegetarian foods were used for the accommodation of guests. A bill for 54 fish supplied to the retreat, dated October 27, 1892, stipulates, "Payable in U.S. Gold Coin."

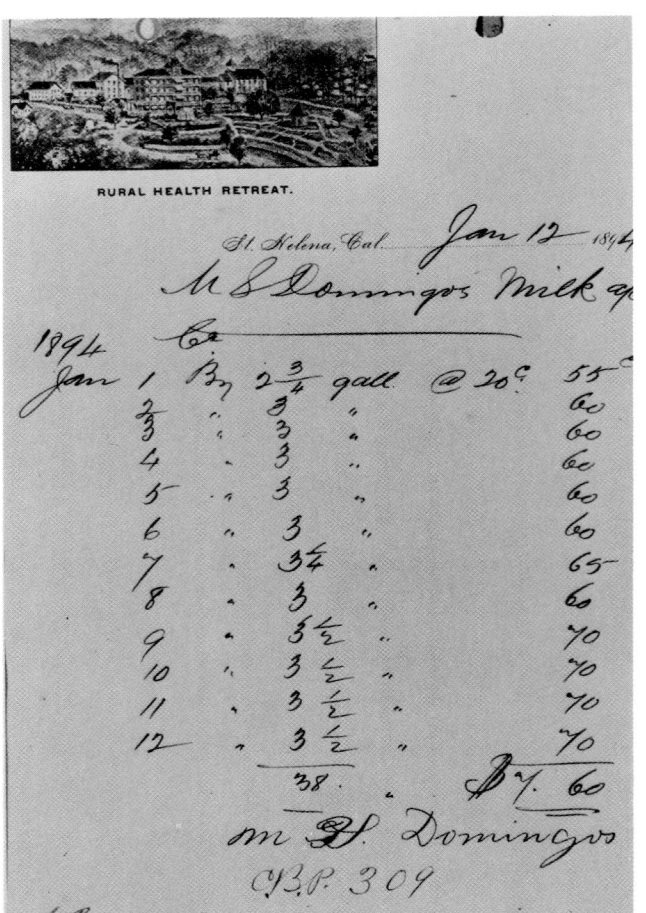

An invoice for thirty-eight gallons of milk indicates that the price was twenty cents a gallon in 1894.

Another Kellogg, Another San

Rural Health Retreat graduated many a class of Nurses

Mamie Hanson-Pickett
graduate of Saint Helena's first class of nurses in 1895.

Good-bye, quiet hillside; good-bye, pleasant home;
Reluctant we leave thee, 'mid strangers to roam;
But the Master has called us; his voice we obey,
In labor for others his love to repay.
  His gentle voice, haste to obey;
  In labor for others his love we repay.
    —From a Rural Health Retreat graduation program

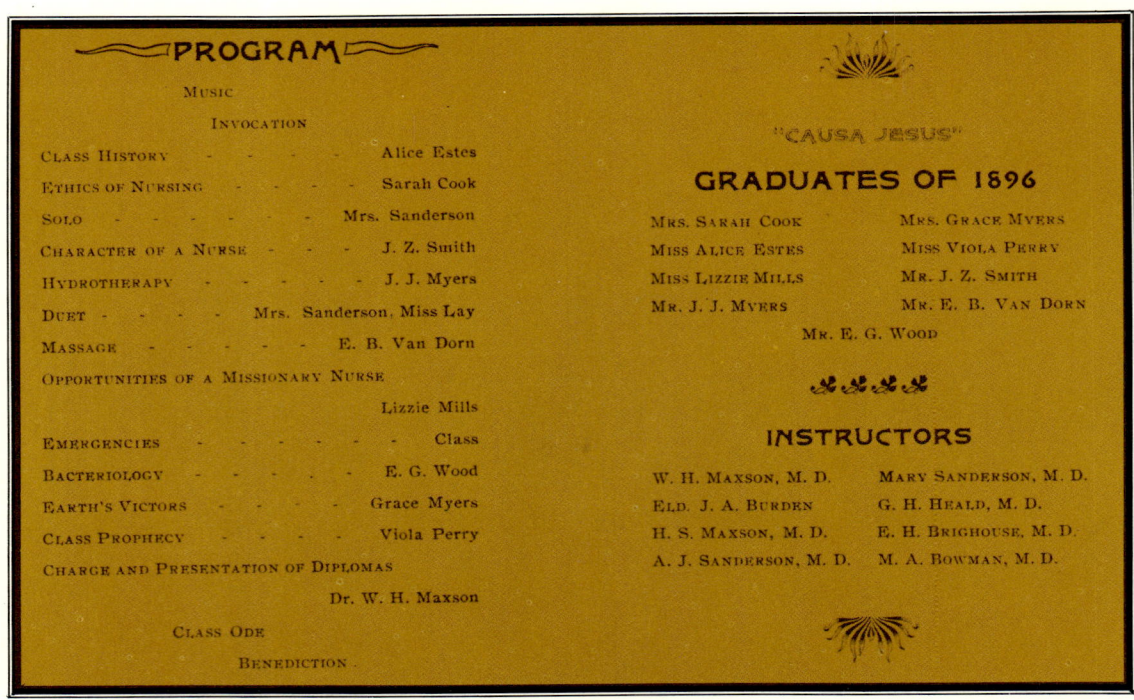

Graduation program, class of 1896.

The graduates, class of 1896.

Nursing class of 1897.

Nursing class of 1900.

STARTING IN 1898, FOR OVER TWENTY YEARS SAINT HELENA SANITARIUM OPERATED A HEALTH FOOD FACTORY

Health food workers pose for picture on loading dock. Below: Minnie Coolidge, Clara Parrott, and Margie Haub package Granola.

A NOSTALGIC LOOK AT A BUSY HEALTH CENTER OF YESTERYEAR

A sanitarium cook.

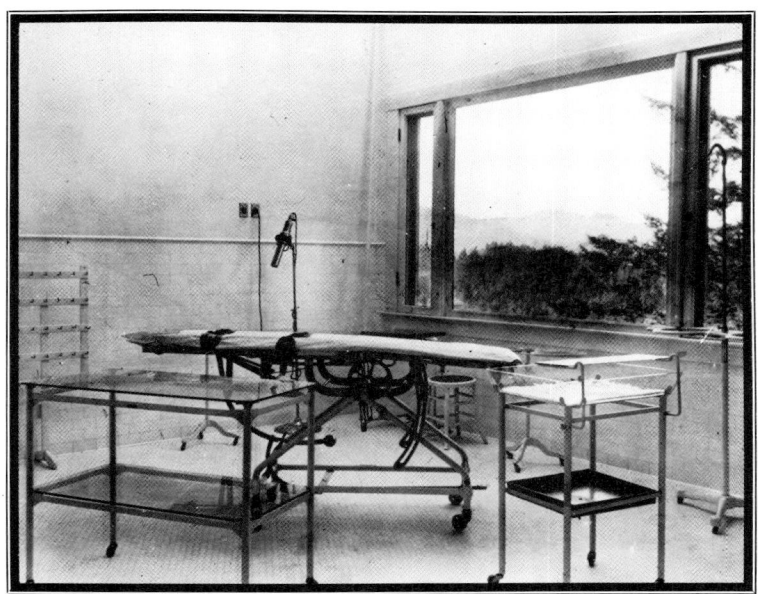

Operating room with a view.

The lobby.

The Vision Bold

Sanitarium stage, 1898.

Supplies arrive after a strenuous uphill haul.

Garbage detail.

The interurban Vallejo-to-Calistoga train brought many a "san" guest as far as Saint Helena.

Three of the best—Maxwell, Stanley Steamer, Oakland—about 1912.

The Vision Bold

Exercise is an important part of sanitarium life.

Men's hydro.

San employees ham it up (about 1930). The boy under the bed is Milton Moore.

124

Saint Helena Sanitarium as it appeared for many years. Now known as Saint Helena Hospital and Health Center, the institution still preserves its country environment.

WHERE KOALA BEARS MUNCHED GUM-TREE LEAVES

HEALTH REFORM LEAPS THE PACIFIC

Sydney Sanitarium opened on January 1, 1903. The building, designed by Dr. Merritt G. Kellogg, cost $25,000 including its eighty acres of land. It stood on the highest point of land in the metropolitan area of Sydney.

Above the sharp call of whipbirds and the caroling of magpies, the clatter of hooves and the grind of steel-clad wheels echoed in Australia's Fox Valley. An open buggy occupied by two women bounced along a gravelly trail until it came to a stream, where the white horse halted, sniffed the air, and refused to go on.

Mary Radley, the driver, turned to her companion, an elderly lady. "Our horse just doesn't like water," she laughed. "My husband will lead him."

A spring cart, drawn by a bay horse and occupied by a party of men, had just arrived on the scene. John Radley led the white horse over the shallow crossing in the shadow of Dog's Head Rock, and the buggy continued its journey.

The panting horse drew the vehicle up a steep incline until the rough forest road leveled out on a partly cleared plateau. Mary halted her buggy near an orange grove and stepped lightly to the ground. She spoke gently to her friend. "Carefully now, Mrs. White, I'll help you down." Then in an animated voice, "Isn't this a lovely place? They say it's 600 feet above sea level."

Ellen White straightened her long dress and adjusted her bonnet. Breathing deeply of the fresh country air, she surveyed the scene before her. The cultivated portion of the land appeared to be fertile and comparatively level, while other sections sloped away to the fringe of the tree-lined watercourse. Here was ample space for fruit trees, vegetable gardens, and cow pastures.

Much of the property, however, was hidden by tall eucalyptus forest, the haunt of koala bears and laughing kookaburras. From the highest elevation, one could catch a view of Sydney Town, a dozen miles away.

Ellen White breathed again the tang of eucalyptus and the fragrance of orange blossom. "Yes, Mary," she said, "this is indeed a grand place—just the right situation for a sanitarium. Here, amidst the beauties of nature, far from the noise of the city, dedicated doctors and nurses can treat the sick and bring balm to troubled spirits. This is the place for a medical institution."

Mrs. White had traveled from her "Sunnyside" home at Cooranbong, eighty miles away, especially to inspect this property. Her friend, Mary Radley, met her at Thornleigh railroad station, and the two women had driven through the deep bushland to the tract of land in question. Several churchmen also made the trip, including Ellen White's son, William, and A. G. Daniells, who had followed with John Radley in the cart.

In 1899, Sydney, with its 450,000 people, was a little over one hundred years old, while the cities of Melbourne and Adelaide boasted only half that age. At the turn of the century, Australia had a population of about 2,500,000, much of it built up by the gold rush of the 1850's. Sailing ships jostled with the newfangled steamships in the chief ports, and horse-drawn wagons still rattled on ill-paved streets.

The Seventh-day Adventist Church organization in Australia was born in 1885 with the arrival of American evangelists S. N. Haskell, J. O. Corliss, and M. C. Israel; Henry L. Scott, a printer, and William Arnold, a colporteur. Ellen Gould White, writer and spiritual leader and now an elderly widow, had a special burden for Australia. In 1891 she came to the land "down under" for a few years to lend her support and guidance to those founders of the infant church in Australia.

Believing the gospel of good health to be an important part of their world commission, Australian Adventists began small health homes and treatment rooms in various centers. Lack of money and trained personnel hampered their early efforts but did not deter them from trying.

Two Australians, Mr. and Mrs. A. W. Semmens, having graduated in nursing at Battle Creek Sanitarium, returned to Sydney in 1895 to begin work. They rented a small cottage at Ashfield for less than a dollar a week, and here they began their treatments. Their list of equipment included an electric bathtub, a massage table, a sitz bath, a gas burner, and a bucket for fomentations.

The first patient was a lady crippled with rheumatoid arthritis. To increase patronage, the Semmens husband-wife team canvassed the district from door to door, telling the people of their work and facilities. These were days of pioneering, poverty, struggle.

Despite the skepticism of some as to Adventist water-healing methods, patronage at the Ashfield center increased. Soon the Semmenses needed larger premises.

In the suburb of Summer Hill, a sixteen-room house known as "Meaford" stood vacant. This mansion, with its rental of five dollars per week, seemed too big a responsibility to shoulder, but the two missionaries visited Ellen White at Cooranbong and sought her counsel. Mrs. White encouraged them to secure the larger building; she even offered to rent and furnish one of the rooms for her personal use when visiting Sydney.

"Meaford" on Gower Street, Summer Hill, opened for health treatments in January, 1897. At first, there were no Adventist doctors in Australia, but a local physician who had seen the success of the Semmenses' methods offered professional support to the struggling institution. This same year a nurse-training program started

Mary Radley drove Ellen White in this buggy to inspect the Wahroonga site in 1899. Seated in the buggy are three Radley boys, Alf, Jack, and Clive.

at Summer Hill with a class of six—Mary Pallant, Lizzie Hubbard, Mimie Steel, Louis and Arthur Currow, and Carl Ulrich.

The tiny medical center, at first known simply as the "Health Home," acquired new dignity with the arrival from Battle Creek of Doctor Edgar R. Caro and several trained nurses. Now the institution's name was changed to "Medical and Surgical Sanitarium."

In 1898, Dr. Caro reported: "We cannot doubt for one moment that the sanitarium will go from success to success.... The entire institution has been placed on a higher scientific plane. A physician has taken charge of the medical and surgical work.... A thoroughly competent chemist and microscopist is at the head of a new complete laboratory of investigation." Dr. Caro claimed that the sanitarium was more advanced than anything of its kind in Australia. In due course, they rented two more buildings on Gower Street to accommodate a growing number of patients and staff.

Even so, few of the patients could afford to pay proper fees, and the medical missionaries struggled to find money for necessary expansion and equipment. In an appeal for funds, Dr. Caro wrote, "Two hundred pounds would build and equip a three-room bath and treatment house, with eight additional bedrooms in the upper story."

In 1899, church leaders decided to expand the health program to the Colony of South Australia. Mr. and Mrs. Semmens and Mary Pallant were asked to go to Adelaide to pioneer the medical work. They opened treatment rooms in Victoria Square, in the heart of town.

The people of Adelaide proved to be conservative and self-satisfied, and patronage was often meager. Despite its important-sounding name, the "Electro-Hydropathic Institute" barely paid its way. But this did not discourage the Adventist leaders in Adelaide. The work grew, and a decade later they opened a suburban sanitarium to serve the city.

By the year 1899, the church leaders felt that the time had come to establish a truly representative sanitarium and hospital in Sydney. F. L. Sharp, then business manager at Summer Hill, worked with others in finding a suitable site. John Wessels, a man with sanitarium experience in South Africa, came to Sydney to help with the search.

They inspected the tree-lined regions north of the harbor, and a property of eight acres at Pymble, but neither area met their needs. Now the committee gave consideration to an eighty-acre property on the wooded heights of Wahroonga.

The natural surroundings made this an ideal site for a health institution, but some felt that patients would not come to a place buried so deeply in the Wahroonga wilderness. However, all were charmed with the bushland aspect, and with Ellen White's endorsement, "This is the place," the decision was made. She advised the brethren to step forward boldly with plans for the sanitarium, although the treasury was bare. The money would be found when needed, she said.

Mr. and Mrs. Geiss, patients at Summer Hill Sanitarium, donated the necessary $1,600 (converted from pounds to Australian dollars) to purchase the Wahroonga land. This was a wonderful start, but the men who had committed themselves to build a large sanitarium faced an almost impossible task. The small church membership was already heavily committed to other projects, such as the new Avondale School for Christian Workers at Cooranbong. How would the sanitarium board raise the money for this bold new project?

About this time, Dr. Merritt G. Kellogg arrived from a term of missionary service in Tonga, and he was asked to design the new Wahroonga Sanitarium. He drew up plans for a 100-bed multi-storied hospital expected to cost $16,000—a fortune in those pioneering days.

At a meeting held at Cooranbong, Ellen White spoke with her usual enthusiasm:

"The sanitarium at Summer Hill as it is now does not properly represent the grand and ennobling work we have to do for the Master. . . . We must begin with a building that will accommodate one hundred patients, and then as the Lord gives prosperity, we shall enlarge, if the Spirit leads in that direction. . . . We are to do the very best we can. We must have a sanitarium, and we must have it out of the city, in a convenient location, where there is plenty of water, because we use water in the place of drugs. The sanitarium is to be located in a restful place, where trams are not passing all the time. It should be away from the smoke of the chimneys of the city, where the atmosphere is as pure as can be found. We can be in touch with Sydney, and yet be out of Sydney. . . .

John and Mary Radley, early Australian Seventh-day Adventists, and parents of nine children.

Two trained nurses, Alfred W. Semmens and his wife, opened the first Adventist treatment rooms in Australia. Later, they returned to America and Semmens studied medicine at Loma Linda, graduating in 1915.

The Vision Bold

In 1895 Mr. and Mrs. Semmens, Australians trained as nurses at Battle Creek Sanitarium, rented "Beechwood Cottage" in Ashfield, a Sydney suburb, for seventy-five cents a week. Thus began Adventist medical work in Australia.

In 1897 a sixteen-room mansion known as "Meaford" was rented and established as a "Health Home," and later as a sanitarium. Dr. E. R. Caro was medical superintendent.

Construction of Sydney Sanitarium was completed in 1903. This is the earliest photograph of the large structure.

"I call upon you this day to help us. . . . He has said, 'Build a sanitarium,' and a sanitarium we are going to build. He is going to help us to do this. We are going to call upon all to take hold and do what they can. The Lord's blessing will rest on the work if we only have a willing mind. God has always helped us, and He will continue to help us."

Pastor E. W. Farnsworth pledged $100 toward the project, and Mrs. White pledged $200. Others followed, until nearly $2,000 was pledged. Building commenced.

The sanitarium at Wahroonga was of wood. Frequently during construction, money ran out and local merchants furnished lumber and other supplies on credit. When payment fell due, the money was somehow found.

Dr. Daniel Kress, medical director, recalled the time when the treasury had no funds and it appeared the building work must be halted. He feared it would take many years to finish the sanitarium. Already, some were calling it a "white elephant." In deep distress, Dr. Kress decided to travel to Tasmania and visit an old member who had given large sums to the church before.

Arriving at Mr. Murfett's farm, Dr. Kress visited for some time, but was reluctant to mention money. Eventually, Murfett asked, "Well, don't you need some money to aid in the building of the sanitarium?"

"Yes," admitted Dr. Kress. "The work is at a standstill because of lack of funds."

"Can you use $4,000?" Murfett inquired.

The doctor could hardly believe his ears, or his eyes, for Murfett proceeded to make out the check for $6,000! Once again the zip of handsaws and the clang of hammers rang through the glades of Wahroonga.

Before the new building was completed, the lease expired at Summer Hill. As an interim measure, the Drs. Kress (Mrs. was also a physician) and the others moved the medical work and the nurse-training school to Cooranbong and occupied the "Health Retreat," a building used to accommodate returned missionaries. Here they found many opportunities to practice the healing arts.

Associating closely with the Kresses at this time was a young student, Margheurita Freeman, who later became the first Adventist lady to graduate in medicine at an Australian university. Late in 1902, Margheurita moved with the "Retreat" family to Wahroonga and the new sanitarium.

Although the building was not yet completed,

the doctors and their team moved in to prepare for the grand opening. The painting of the rooms was not finished, but all worked feverishly to have at least a portion of the building ready for patients. The Sanitarium opened its doors on January 1, 1903.

Margheurita Freeman later recollected: "When the Sydney Sanitarium opened, the building was not completed—only the ground floor. It was lit by gas and the only heating was by wood fires in iron grates. Only the rooms needed to accommodate incoming patients were finished and furnished.

"The rest of us—the staff—lived on the third floor. We had hessian [burlap] on the floor. The windows were not in, and hessian hung in doorways. We had oil lamps. During 1903, the building was slowly finished."

Before the official opening date, the Sydney Sanitarium had accepted its first paying patient. Mr. Lewis Butler, a businessman and property owner in the Wahroonga district, fell seriously ill with rheumatic fever, and was given forty-eight hours to live. The sick man's family had heard of a new hospital being built in the backwoods of Wahroonga, and in desperation placed him in a horse-drawn cab and transported him over the rough, stony roads to the still unfinished sanitarium.

At first, they were told that the institution could not yet receive patients, but their pleas prevailed and the staff accepted Lewis Butler. They found room for him as last-minute hammering continued, and the smell of fresh paint wafted through the corridors. Dr. Kress and his nursing staff, through God's intervention, they said, succeeded in saving Butler's life.

Lewis Butler was deeply impressed with the ideals of the institution and the people who served there. During convalescence, he read some literature, and after taking Bible studies, accepted the Adventist faith. For the next thirty years, Butler gave of his business experience and much of his wealth to the church. Over the years, four generations of Butlers have contributed to the organized work of the church in Australasia. (Lewis Butler's grandson, Lance L. Butler, currently treasurer of the Australasian Division of Seventh-day Adventist, helped steer the finances of the church during the multimillion dollar rebuilding of the Sydney Sanitarium and Hospital in 1971-73.)

Since the first Summer Hill class, more than a thousand nurses have graduated from the sanitarium school of nursing. They have served in Australia and New Zealand, and as medical missionaries in a score of overseas countries.

Ellen White never saw the finished building. Seventy-three years old, she returned to America. There, from Elmshaven, she maintained a lively interest in the expanding work of Seventh-day Adventists "down under."

In 1905, she wrote from Elmshaven: "Sanitariums should be established near such cities as Melbourne and Adelaide. . . . Do not discourage those who are trying to advance this work." The Australian brethren responded, as they usually did, with faith and action.

In 1908, they built a health institution at Warburton, Victoria, forty-eight miles from Melbourne. This developed into the Warburton Sanitarium and Hospital, with 110 beds.

New Zealand was not forgotten. The year 1898 had seen the opening of a humble "Health Home" in the city of Christchurch. This grew into the Christchurch Sanitarium in 1900. The institution limped along, often without adequate medical personnel, and finally closed in 1921. However, over a half century later, in January, 1974, the New Zealand Adventist Hospital, an ultramodern health unit situated in a bayside suburb of Auckland, opened its doors to the public.

The Adventists "down under" had a burden also to conduct their health and healing ministry beyond the walls of their sanitariums. In the early 1900's, they established Helping Hand Mission, Helping Hand Woodyard, and Old Folks' Home and Orphanage, all in Melbourne; Rescue Home in Adelaide; Health Home and Helping Hand Laundry in Perth; Gospel Medical School at Bondi; Medical Mission at Newcastle; and Bethany Rescue Home at Napier, New Zealand. Unfortunately, these worthwhile projects did not survive the early famine of personnel and funds.

Another field of endeavor ultimately fared better. While still minuscule in size, the Australian church lifted its gaze from its own needs to the island world of the vast South Pacific. Before the turn of the century, a few Adventist pioneers from America had visited certain islands, some of them sailing on the mission ship *Pitcairn*. Dr. and Mrs. J. E. Caldwell landed in Rarotonga in 1894, Dr. and Mrs. F. E. Braught in Western Samoa in 1895, and Dr. and Mrs. M. G. Kellogg in Tonga in 1897.

With the dawn of the new century, the Aus-

Before Sanitarium construction was completed, Lewis Butler, at the point of death, was brought to Dr. Daniel H. Kress. The physician took him in and with the Lord's help saved his life. Butler and his family became Adventists, and subsequently four generations of Butlers have produced a small army of denominational workers in Australia.

Dr. and Mrs. Merritt Kellogg (right), after sailing to the South Seas in the Pitcairn, *worked as medical missionaries in Tonga, and came to Australia in 1900, where he designed the Sydney Sanitarium and superintended its construction. The Kelloggs returned to the United States in 1903. With them here are Pastor and Mrs. Hickox and daughter.*

tralasian Union Conference, later the Australasian Division, was assigned the South Pacific area. A task force of missionaries fanned out from the Australian base, few at first, but increasing in number, many of them trained in nursing care at the Sydney Sanitarium and Hospital. So few Adventist physicians were available that for many years the church's medical work in the Pacific Islands was entrusted to the trained nurses. These were mainly husband-and-wife teams who operated front-porch clinics for victims of burns, wounds, ulcers, malaria, yaws, and leprosy.

Some clinics were mobile. The nurses traveled by foot, dugout canoe, and later with a fleet of motor launches and several airplanes. Eventually, small hospitals and clinics, better equipped than the front-porch variety, were established in places like Batuna, Kukudu, and Omaura, though some operated for long periods without the luxury of a resident physician.

In recent years, Aore Adventist Hospital, in the New Hebrides, has operated under the care of a qualified Fijian medical superintendent, Dr. Joeli Taoi.

In 1949, Australian missionary Len H. Barnard built and opened the first Hansenide Hospital in New Guinea. Owned by the government, but manned continuously by a Seventh-day Adventist staff, this unit at Togoba has treated thousands of Hansenide sufferers. Doctors and therapists, using modern control medication and reconstruction surgery, return most leprosy victims to a useful village life.

Another New Guinea medical unit, the Sopas Adventist Hospital, operates its own school of nursing. Baby health clinics conducted in the surrounding villages train native mothers in better baby care. Sopas-trained nurses and medical assistants man aid posts in remote mountain villages, and help staff health units such as Hatzfeldhaven Hansenide Hospital on New Guinea's coast.

Not only the sanitarium idea, but also the health-food philosophy made the trans-pacific pilgrimage and prospered in Australia. In 1897, George Fisher, an Echo Publishing Company employee, received a shipment of Dr. Kellogg's health foods from Battle Creek, Michigan. Naturally, there was little demand for the strange products even among Adventists, who had scarcely heard of such foods before. But the publishing-house staff did try the products and ordered more.

Then someone remembered that four years before, at North Brighton camp meeting, Ellen White had envisioned and strongly urged the establishing of a health-food industry in Australia. With the same willingness to step into the unknown that had marked other ventures, the church leaders decided to manufacture the foods in Australia.

Without money or know-how, what they *did* have was a prodigious amount of belief in an ideal. In December, 1897, they formed a committee to set up a food factory. They rented a rundown bakery in North Fitzroy, Melbourne, and with a few items of primitive equipment they began to grind and mix and bake.

Fortunately, the committee had the wisdom to import Mr. E. C. Halsey, an experienced baker from the Battle Creek plant. Soon the factory was turning out Australian-made Granola, Caramel Cereal, and peanut butter as good as the imported product, only less expensive and a lot fresher!

The Melbourne plant was considered to be experimental. The committee hoped to build a large permanent factory when they could find a suitable site. In the meantime, they place consignments of the foods with various agencies, Summer Hill Sanitarium being one of the sales outlets.

Even so, the Sanitarium Health Food Agency, as it was then named, found the going hard. People had to be educated to use the new foods. The small factory operated at a loss as shelves piled high with unsold stocks. Some thought that the whole project should be scrapped.

Apparently the infant health-food industry was doomed to failure. Commerce in general was bad at the time. A land-boom failure in Victoria had closed banks and spread pessimism.

But the committee refused to fold up the operation. They merely voted to give all health-food employees a vacation without pay until the market demanded more of the product. They then set about finding the site for a large factory, for hadn't Ellen White forecast that the business would prosper and become a great asset?

In August, 1898, G. W. Morse arrived from the United States to help steer the health-food industry. He, with several others, helped search for a new factory site. Some felt the plant should be located near the Wahroonga Sanitarium in Sydney, but Cooranbong was finally chosen. Ellen White had recommended that the food factory be built near the Avondale School so that students could be employed there and earn their school expenses. Both institutions would benefit from this arrangement.

The financially harassed Avondale school board was happy to sell some of its land on Dora Creek, together with a sawmill building. The food-company men promptly set about converting the mill into a food-production plant. They made thousands of bricks from clay on the property, and fired the bricks with local wood. They built a huge oven to bake the products they hoped to sell.

They had imported some food-production machinery from the United States, and they hired students to manufacture, pack, and ship the products for market. They used barges on Dora Creek to transport the goods to the railhead. The Cooranbong area had become a beehive of industry, even if not a very large or prosperous beehive.

The promised era of great assets and rich rewards lay far ahead. By 1904, the Cooranbong plant was $11,000 in debt. The main problem was lack of marketing. The general public did not know the foods existed. To overcome this problem, the company decided to open retail outlets in the form of vegetarian cafes and food shops in the major cities.

George Fisher, then manager of the Sanitarium Health Food Company's retail shop and cafe business, recalls the financial struggles of those pioneering days. They opened the first outlet in Sydney and rented a dilapidated building that had been a Cobb & Co. coachhouse at the corner of Castlereagh and Hunter Streets. Renovating the place on a shoestring budget, they opened for business. Patronage slowly developed, but not without much hard work and "turning over every penny before it was spent."

When there was no money on payday for employees, they waited for it—then voluntarily handed some of it back. There had to be some money in the cashbox to buy supplies for the cafe kitchen. George Fisher and others pushed a handcart through the streets of Sydney to the markets to buy vegetables. Two girl employees secretly obtained a key to the premises so that they could start work at six in the morning without telling the manager!

Early nursing staff of the Adelaide Sanitarium. Left to right: Hannah Williams, Minnie Reeves, William F. Rudge, and Mrs. Esther McDonald. All graduated from Sydney Sanitarium.

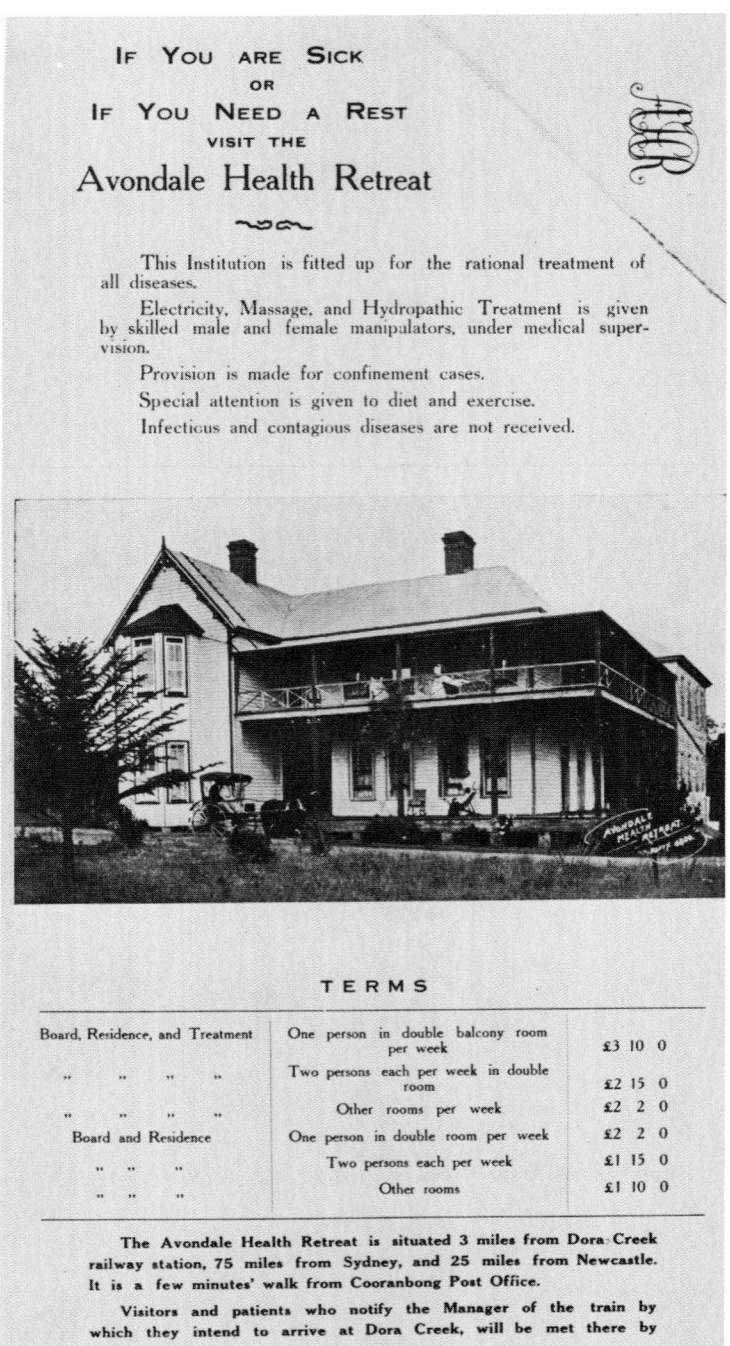

Advertisement for Avondale Health Retreat.

Adelaide Sanitarium, established in 1908.

As the dining-room business improved, it was necessary to rent a storeroom next door and knock out a wall to enlarge the dining area. On August 19, 1906, a hundred Sydney church members came to a dinner at the cafe to commemorate the opening of the enlarged premises. After the meal, the staff presented a program. They gave a pearl-shell model of a sailboat containing twenty-five gold sovereigns to the superintendent of the Island Mission Field, Elder Edward H. Gates.

Those golden coins, worth more than $1,000 today as collector's items, represented much sacrifice on the part of those who made the gift possible. G. S. Fisher wrote: "This was the beginning of financial assistance for our island mission work from the Sanitarium Health Food Company."

The health-food men learned better ways to manufacture their products. If they lacked

Christchurch Sanitarium ad which appeared in Good Health June 1, 1902.

necessary machinery, they designed and built it. They learned better ways of packaging and marketing. Sanitarium Brand products became household words throughout Australia and New Zealand. The biggest public breakthrough came with breakfast cereals—Granose, Weet Bix, and flakes. The company's food-research and quality-control laboratory, in co-operation with the factory, developed better corn flakes.

Twelve large factories now manufacture "Sanitarium" products throughout Australia and New Zealand. Seventeen wholesale warehouses and depots distribute to supermarket chains. Eleven retail offices co-ordinate sixty-five Sanitarium-owned retail stores and food bars.

From one struggling bakehouse in a back street of Melbourne has grown a multimillion dollar industry which has made massive contributions to the church's medical and educational program. The impossible dream has come true.

Helping Hand Wood Yard, Melbourne.

Dr. Margheurita M. Freeman, seated at left, graduated in medicine at Sydney University in 1911, the first Adventist lady to earn a degree in medicine in Australia. She appears here with her staff, and with the hospital cat, at the Avondale Health Retreat. Soon afterward she married Dr. T. A. Sherwin, and the two physicians took charge of the Sydney Sanitarium until 1931.

Sydney Sanitarium directors during the first year of operation: Drs. Daniel and Lauretta Kress, medical directors; Elder and Mrs. G. A. Irwin; an unidentified lady; and Elder and Mrs. John Burden.

In 1920 the Sydney Sanitarium purchased an omnibus to carry patients and staff to and from the rail station.

The Vision Bold

Sydney group with sanitarium-born infants in 1921. Dr. Margheurita is seated at left.

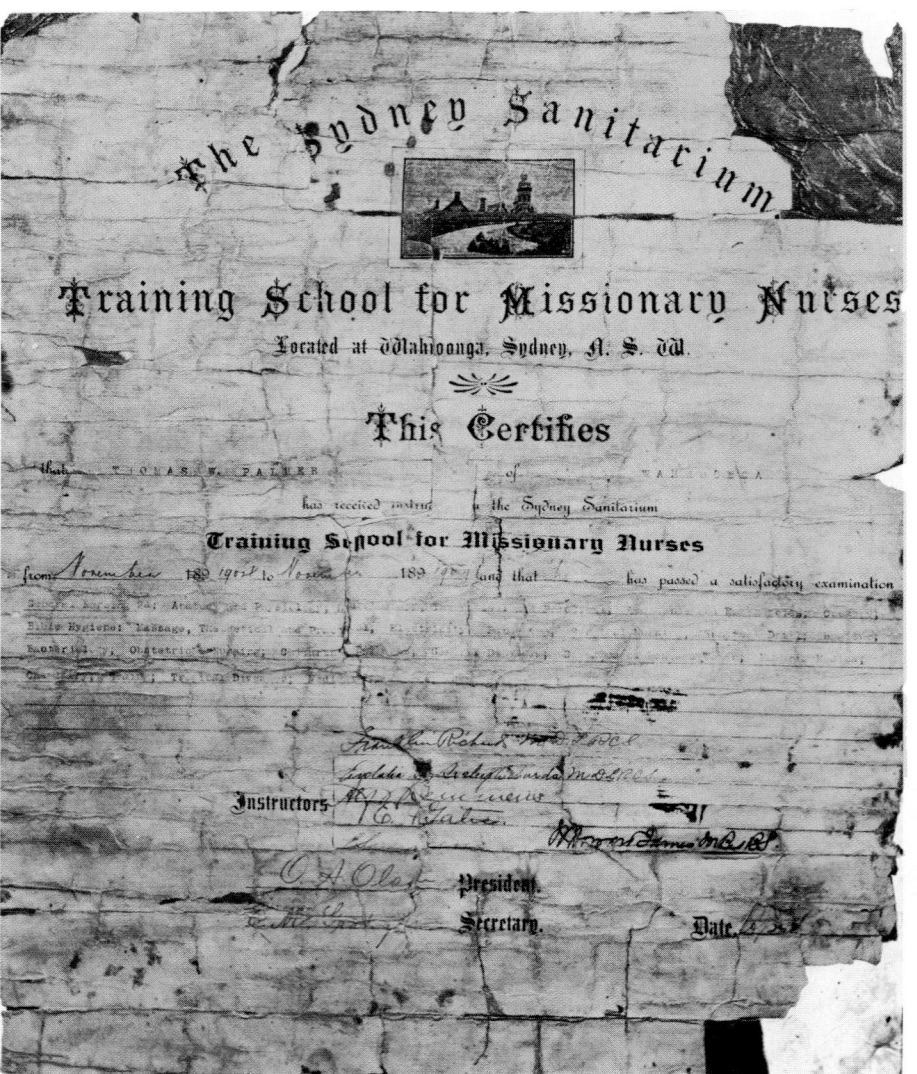

Not a Dead Sea scroll, but an early nursing certificate presented to Thomas W. Palmer in 1907. Palmer's son Reuben was the first baby born in Sydney Sanitarium, in 1903.

During T. A. Sherwin's regime as medical director at Sydney, nurses spent Saturday nights doing "physical jerks" just in case they did not get enough exercise climbing stairs and walking long sanitarium corridors.

Like its sister institutions in the United States, the sanitarium grew rapidly and sprouted wings. This north wing was added in 1917.

The Vision Bold

AUSTRALIA AND NEW ZEALAND ADVENTIST

One of the earliest Australian health food ads, used before the turn of the century.

As a young man, George S. Fisher opened the first shipment of Battle Creek health food and distributed them. He later managed the Sanitarium Health Food Company, and served two terms as manager of the Sydney Sanitarium.

Part of the staff of Sydney's first vegetarian cafe in the early 1900's. The tall young man at the rear left is A. W. Cormack, later a General Conference leader in Washington.

Where Koala Bears Munched Gum-Tree Leaves

EVELOPED A STRONG HEALTH FOOD INDUSTRY.

The company's letterhead.

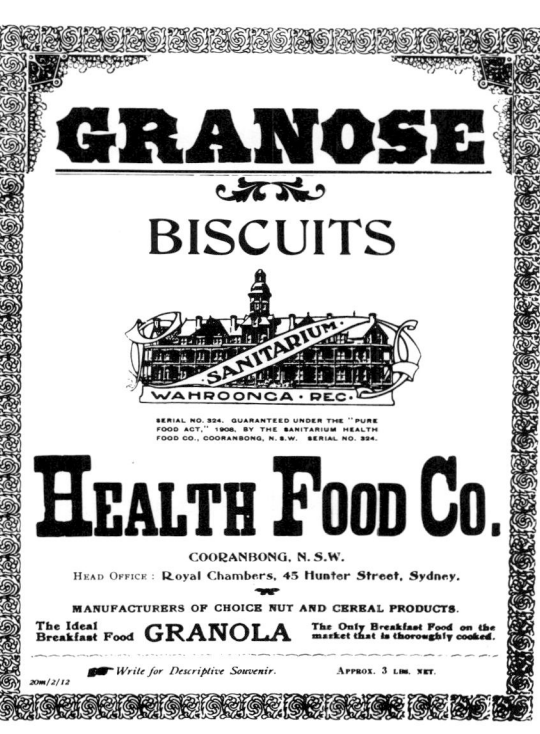

Early labels for Sanitarium health foods.

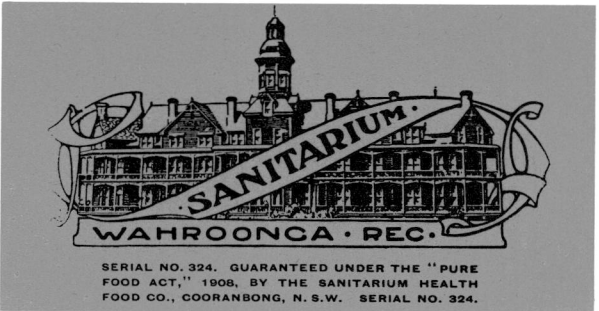

The trademark.

143

The Vision Bold

Loading Sanitarium Health foods onto barges at Dora Creek, New South Wales, for transport to the railhead. In background is the Cooranbong food factory as it appeared in the 1920's.

The Christchurch, New Zealand food factory in the 1920's.

Where Koala Bears Munched Gum-Tree Leaves

Fleet of Sanitarium Health Food trucks filled with Weet Bix and Granose biscuits deliver their products in 1930.

GOD WILL GIVE THE THIRSTY ELEPHANT A DRINK

THANKS TO A MIRACLE WELL, PARADISE VALLEY SPRINGS TO LIFE

own the well diggers went "through the dry earth, where the dust flew more than twenty feet below the surface." They struck clay and, after many weeks, gravel and stone. At eighty feet, the weary crew were shoveling out only dry dirt and gravel. Somewhat discouraged, Mr. Salem Hamilton, the contractor, sent for Ellen White. On arriving, she asked, "What are you going to do, Brother Hamilton?"

"I have a question to ask *you*," he answered. "If you will answer that, I will give you my answer. Did the Lord tell you to buy this property?"

"Yes! Yes!" Ellen White replied. Three times I was shown that we should secure this particular property."

"All right," Mr. Hamilton said, "I have my answer. The Lord would not give us an elephant without providing water for it to drink."

So the digging proceeded, but with a drift at the bottom in a new direction. Late the next night, when no sign of moisture had yet appeared, the tired digger at the bottom of the well called out, "Mr. Palmer, would you be afraid to come down? I think there is water not far away."

Mr. Palmer descended and heard it distinctly, "like the tinkle of a bell or the sound of a small waterfall in the depths of a forest." His account continues: "On returning to the surface, I almost immediately heard a shout from the attendant to let down the bucket. The digger had struck a vigorous blow, and his pick had broken through into a fine stream of water as large as a man's arm. That night the water rose eighteen feet in the well."

Early the following morning, November 23, 1904, Palmer and W. C. White called at Ellen White's room to excitedly announce the good news. Writing the next day to her grandchildren, Mrs. White said:

"Early yesterday morning Bro. Palmer came to my room in company with your father [Elder W. C. White] and told us there was 15 feet of water in the well. This morning there is twenty feet of water and their tools at the bottom of the well. I cannot express to you how glad we all are made. Plenty of water for all purposes! This cannot be estimated by gold or by silver. Water means life. . . . The Lord has answered all our expectations, and we shall have reason for thanksgiving. . . . I want to praise the Lord with heart and soul and will."

Back in the 1880's when rail service had come to the San Diego, California, area, invalids and convalescents began to stream in from the East. Even the earliest adventurers had recognized the health promoting effects of the moderate temperatures, the sunshine, and the sea breezes. They testified, "Here the sick recover!"

Here Dr. Anna Mary (nee Longshore) Potts founded a sanitarium in 1888, a four-story, thirty-eight-bed institution located on a twenty-acre-plus promontory of land. She spent $25,000 for the main building and added a six-room residence and a stable and carriage house. Dr. Potts, a woman of humanitarian instincts and considerable wealth, had been a member of the first graduating class of the Philadelphia Women's Medical College.

To set off the impressive building properly, she invested large sums of money to lay out the spacious grounds of her sanitarium with ornamental shrubbery and shade trees. The slopes of the hills were gracefully terraced, and olive, orange, and lemon trees planted. On December 6, 1888, the sanitarium opened for guests.

For several years, the Potts Sanitarium prospered, but before the mid-1890's prolonged drought afflicted the San Diego area. Little by little, wells failed all over the valley, and eventually the water supply in the reservoir behind the huge Sweetwater Dam dwindled away. Fields turned from green to tan; shrubs and flowers died. Owners of scores of ranches were ruined. Residents grew discouraged, and many decided that the area had no future. Those who were lucky sold out and moved to other areas. Real estate values plummeted. Many families simply moved away, leaving their homes deserted.

New wells were sunk throughout the valley, but only a few yielded water, and in meager amounts. The rest proved so dry that a pebble dropped into their depths would ring out against the stony sides and clink hopelessly on a rocky bottom.

The water supply of the Potts Sanitarium held up for a time, then faltered. The grounds grew barren, the trees withered. Patients and guests departed. Dr. Potts, discouraged, mortgaged the property for $14,000. She arranged with her wealthy uncle, Dr. T. H. Harrison of New York, to assume ownership of the property. For a time, he paid the expenses, while Dr. Potts made an extended tour of Europe. Then in 1895, Dr. Harrison closed the sanitarium.

During the next eight or nine years of drought, Potts Sanitarium was utterly deserted. Wayfarers and vandals marred the walls and knocked out the windows. The doors stood ajar; and, according to a lady who visited the building, countless bats had taken up residence in the top floor "flying over our heads so thick we had to fight them off."

During this drought, in 1900, Ellen White received strong impressions, which she believed were from God, that this drought-stricken region would flourish again and make an ideal location for a sanitarium and hospital of the Battle Creek type. She had recently returned from Australia and settled in Elmshaven. Once, before she left Australia, and three times by 1901, Mrs. White had been shown in vision a property in the San Diego area suitable for a medical center. In 1902, she wrote:

"I have been shown that in southern California there are properties for sale on which buildings are already erected that could be utilized for our work, and that such properties will be offered to us at much less than their original cost."

In 1901, at a meeting in Oakland, Mrs. White had met a young physician, T. S. Whitelock, of San Diego. He had graduated from the American Medical Missionary College in Battle Creek. She told him that she "had been shown a property near San Diego" which she wanted Adventists to have for a medical missionary center. She urged Dr. Whitelock to see what he could do to locate this property.

Mrs. White also wrote to the California Conference leaders urging action. Thus earnestly exhorted to embark on such a project, the Southern California Conference opened a health-food store and vegetarian cafeteria in San Diego. Soon afterwards, Drs. Whitelock and Sophie Johnson opened a medical office and treatment rooms at the corner of Fourth and C Streets, San Diego. Patients flocked in, and the effort proved a success from the beginning.

One of Dr. Whitelock's patients, Mr. John E. Boal, a National City businessman, told the doctor of a place in Paradise Valley that might be secured which would admirably serve as an Adventist sanitarium. Mr. Boal gave Dr. Whitelock the address of Dr. Harrison, the New York owner. In response to a letter, Harrison replied that he had "$28,000 in the property, that he had been paying the taxes and all on it for six or seven years, and that he wanted $28,000 for it." The Whitelocks replied that they had been out and looked at the property, that they were much interested, would like to have it, that they could not raise that much money, but would see what they could do.

With Mrs. White's encouragement, the Whitelocks continued the correspondence with Dr. Harrison for several months. The result was a gradual reduction in the price asked for the Potts property. Finally, Dr. Harrison offered the entire estate for $8,000. At that point, the Whitelocks wrote Mrs. White enthusiastically of their negotiations.

The Whitelocks also wrote to Dr. John Harvey Kellogg in Battle Creek, inviting him to inspect the Potts property as a possible branch of the Battle Creek institution. Dr. Kellogg came promptly and showed great interest. On leaving by train, he promised to return to continue the negotiations. But as Kellogg's train neared Chicago, he received a telegram with the shocking news that the Battle Creek Sanitarium was in flames. He reached home in time to see only the smoking ruins. Thereafter, he was fully occupied with the rebuilding of that famous institution and gave no further consideration to the Potts property.

The attention of the local Adventist conference leaders, as well as the General Conference, was called to the available Potts Sanitarium. The local conference officials showed enough interest to visit the place; but, due to the continuing drought and the state of conference finances, they did nothing toward its purchase.

In September, 1902, after the Los Angeles Adventist camp meeting, Mrs. White, her son, Elder W. C. White, and other workers visited the San Diego area.

Mrs. White later said: "In the building offered us by Mrs. Potts, it seemed to me we found about all that we could ask. Here was a well-constructed . . . building, with broad verandas, standing on a pleasant rise of ground, and overlooking a beautiful valley. . . . Besides the main building there is a good stable, and also a six-room cottage which can be fitted up for helpers. . . . There are about twenty-two acres of land. About one half of this was once planted to fruit trees, but during the long drought . . . all the trees died except the ornamental trees and shrubbery around the buildings and about seventy olive trees on the terraces."

Learning, probably from Dr. Whitelock, that the property was available, Mrs. White wrote the president of the Southern California Conference:

"I believe that the Lord has kept this place for us, and that He will open the way for us to secure it. I never saw a building offered for sale that was better adapted for sanitarium work. If this place were fixed up, it would be just like the place shown me by the Lord." But the conference leaders then, and for some years later, were not ready to cooperate.

In December, 1902, when Mrs. White learned that the price of the Potts property was down to $11,000, she wrote to Dr. Whitelock urging him "to take steps to secure it." But without funds, the doctor could make no offer, though he did continue correspondence with Dr. Harrison and his agents. In the summer of 1903, the price was down to $8,000. Whitelock again appealed to the conference officials, who remained unconvinced.

Dr. Whitelock, fearful that this unprecedented opportunity would slip through their fingers, wrote Mrs. White on December 30, 1903, "The Golden Opportunity has come to secure this property."

Finally, in January, 1904, Dr. Whitelock again wrote Mrs. White to say that the mortgages could be bought up for $6,000 "and perhaps less." This seemed to Mrs. White to be an offer too good to let pass. But she knew the conference

God Will Give the Thirsty Elephant a Drink

San Diego was a yeasty place in the boom years of the 1880's. Above: downtown traffic. Middle: town dudes, members of the Cuyamaca Club. Right: an Electric Rapid Transit car.

The incredible Coronado Hotel completed in 1888, the same year as the Potts Sanitarium, was built of redwood. With 399 rooms, it typified the boom town that was San Diego.

could do nothing, and she went to the bank and borrowed $2,000 toward the price. Mrs. Josephine Gotzian, a well-to-do elderly widow, lived nearby. She was a good friend of Mrs. White; moreover, she still had considerable money. Sensing the urgency of the situation, Mrs. White did not hesitate to lay the situation before her friend and frankly appeal for help. Mrs. Gotzian advanced another $2,000 to bind the deal.

Meantime, Dr. and Mrs. Whitelock had been bringing interested people to look at this property when they visited San Diego. Mrs. Whitelock tells of one such experience:

"Another couple, Dr. Whitelock, and I were out here on the third floor of this building; and I looked out and saw two ladies come driving up the driveway. I said to my husband, 'Now you see, people have found out what a low price this building is selling for, and they will get it away from us.' He answered, 'Well, don't worry about that. If the Lord wants us to have it, He will keep it for us.' So the ladies . . . came up to the third floor where we were; and we spoke to them, of course. The lady, a Mrs. Doutney from New York, looked around and said, 'This is a pretty nice building, isn't it?' Dr. Whitelock replied, 'Well, it has been, but it is in pretty bad repair right now.' As the conversation went on, she said, 'May I ask who you are?' He answered, 'I am Dr. Whitelock.' The lady exclaimed, 'Why, Dr. Whitelock, you are the very man that Dr. Harrison sent me out here to see about buying this building.' She then asked him if he would come to her hotel that night, which he did. There Mrs. Doutney told him, 'Dr. Harrison is so disgusted with this proposition out here that I think if you would offer him $6,000 cash you could get it.' Dr. Whitelock replied, "Well, I don't know where I could get $6,000 cash, but I do know where I could have $4,000 in sight in two days."

Throughout all these negotiations, and in Mrs. White's various appeals to Elder A. G. Daniells of the General Conference, to the local conference officials and to the Pacific Medical Missionary Association, ran the consistent theme that the sanitarium should be a strong medical-evangelical outpost and that it should be under conference ownership and control. Only after repeated appeals to various denominational organizations proved futile did private individuals take action. Even so, the purchasers held to the conviction that they were holding the property in trust temporarily for the Southern California Conference.

Then the exodus began and "For Sale" signs blossomed in store windows, front yards, and vacant lots. People moved away by the thousands as drought gripped the city.

Like Dr. Whitelock, Mrs. White felt that it was "now or never" in the securing of the Potts property. Having available between them $4,000, the two ladies then learned that up to $600 more would be needed to clear the title and pay back taxes. Mrs. White promptly appealed to Elder and Mrs. J. F. Ballenger, who had just received a "windfall" in the form of an old debt paid. They gladly provided the needed $600. Mrs. White promptly contacted Whitelock; and on January 25, 1904, they telegraphed an offer of $4,000 to New York. Two days later, they received word of acceptance.

This transaction came none too soon. A two days' delay would have lost the property, as other prospective buyers had written an offer of $6,000, and their letter reached New York a few hours after the offer of $4,000 had been accepted. Thus was fulfilled Mrs. White's assurance, "I believe the Lord has kept this place for us and that He will open the way for us to secure it."

Having purchased the property, the new owners proceeded to secure a manager. They made a good choice in Mr. E. R. Palmer, who, for health reasons, had spent several months in Arizona. The Palmers were visiting in San Diego at the time and were approached with the request that they undertake the work of renovating and fitting up the vacant main building for use. Palmer later wrote:

"On the eighteenth of April, 1904, Mrs. Palmer and I came here as caretakers, and for the first few weeks gave our attention largely to legal matters. . . . Eight and one-half acres lying to the east of us, owned by a Mrs. Barrett, was secured for $600, thus making the total cost of the estate about $5,500."

During the ensuing months, the main building was repaired, fitted with electric wiring and lights, and painted throughout. Fourteen rooms were furnished. First-class furniture was bought at very low prices from several wealthy families who were moving away. The windmill and water pipes were renewed.

The searing, blighting drought still prevailed, and many questioned the wisdom of reopening the sanitarium. Indeed, the lack of water was not only the main reason for the low price paid for the property but was also an important factor in the refusal to invest in the project by the denominational organizations that had declined to participate. Obviously, without water the place could be of no practical value.

Never wavering in her confidence that every obstacle would be overcome, Mrs. White was certain that they had found the right place and

Before the Potts Sanitarium was purchased, the Southern California Conference opened a successful health food store and restaurant in San Diego.

that an adequate water supply would be found on the premises. After consulting her co-owners and Dr. Whitelock, she sent out of state for an experienced well digger she knew, a Mr. Hamilton. There was some delay, but during the summer of 1904 Mr. Hamilton arrived and proceeded to assemble the essential equipment and crew. Dr. Whitelock said of this episode, "With what anxiety we surveyed the ground and discussed the possibilities can scarcely be imagined by those who were not present."

As we have already seen, the results bordered on the miraculous. When the diggers struck water at last, an eight-horsepower engine was placed near the well. When the pump, throwing a four-inch stream, could not lower the water level, the well was pronounced a signal success. A 10,000-gallon tank was installed, providing fifty pounds of water pressure. During all the following years, until a municipal water system was installed, this well never once failed to supply the sanitarium with clear, cold water more than adequate for all its needs. And this in spite of the drought which had closed the Potts Sanitarium.

While the well was being dug, Elders Ballenger and Willie White were soliciting aid from the churches of the area. They returned the night water was found with donations of about $1,500.

Earlier in the year, on April 12, 1904, a meeting was called in San Diego to consider the organization and management of the Paradise Valley Sanitarium.

W. C. White, J. F. Ballenger, John A. Burden, F. I. Richardson, Professor E. S. Ballenger, E. R. Palmer, I. O. Johnson, T. S. Whitelock, and Sophie Johnson attended the meeting. They discussed the relationship of the sanitarium to the Southern California Conference of Seventh-day Adventists, and agreed that, until the conference or a medical association could assume ownership, the owners would operate it as a private venture. Each would receive 6 percent interest on his investment. They also agreed to ask the cooperation and moral support of the conference. The local conference committee responded by voting "to give their moral support and cooperation to the enterprise but not to take any financial responsibility or burden." The individuals mentioned above constituted themselves the original board of trustees for the institution, with Elder W. C. White as chairman and E. R. Palmer as secretary. The board appointed Dr. Whitelock medical director.

The board of trustees developed the Paradise Valley Sanitarium Association as a stock company and offered shares for $100 each, bearing 6 percent interest. They raised nearly $12,000 and invested the sum in treatment rooms, medi-

Mrs. Josephine Gotzian—she put up $2,000 to close the deal.

Dr. Anna Potts—she built the Potts Sanitarium.

cal equipment, and other furnishings.

Late in November, 1904, before Mrs. White left, a four-horse team drawing a large, heavy wagon drove in bringing gifts from the churches of San Pasqual and Escondido. This timely donation included potatoes, squash, and canned fruit. Of special importance, the gift included two fine Jersey cows, which in time developed into a dairy herd of more than eighty cows. For many years, the herd supplied the institution with milk and cream.

Before the sanitarium was really ready for patients, a Mrs. Julia Ulrich arrived and insisted on staying. The same lady returned to Paradise Valley Sanitarium in the evening of her life and remained until her passing in 1933 at the age of ninety-two.

"Others arrived," wrote Mrs. White, "before we were ready, and patients continued to come until there were twenty and the workers were kept so busy that the formal opening had to be postponed." Also, within the year, the long drought was broken. All nature seemed to spring to life in the valley, and real estate values rose rapidly.

The formal reopening of the sanitarium with appropriate dedicatory services took place April 24, 1906. Speakers included Elders S. N. Haskell, W. M. Healey, and W. C. White; Professor E. S. Ballenger; Mrs. E. G. White; and

Dr. and Mrs. Whitelock—they pioneered Paradise Valley Sanitarium.

CERTIFICATE
No 1
For Twenty S
Issued to
Ellen G. White
Dated April 1
FROM WHOM TRANSFERRED
Dated
No. ORIGINAL CERTIFICATE	No. ORIGINAL SHARES	No. OF TRANS

Received CERTIFICATE No.
For
this day of

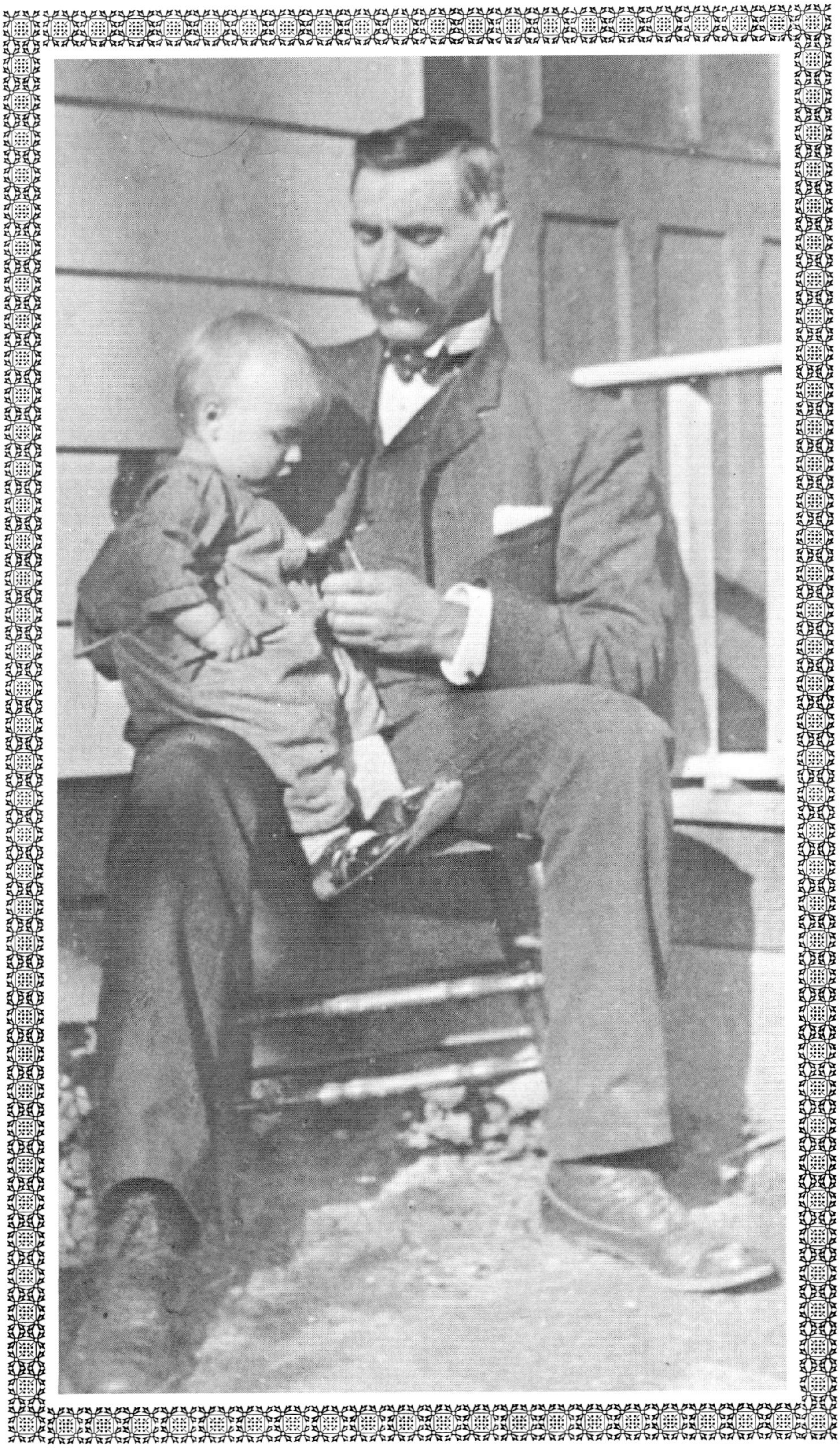

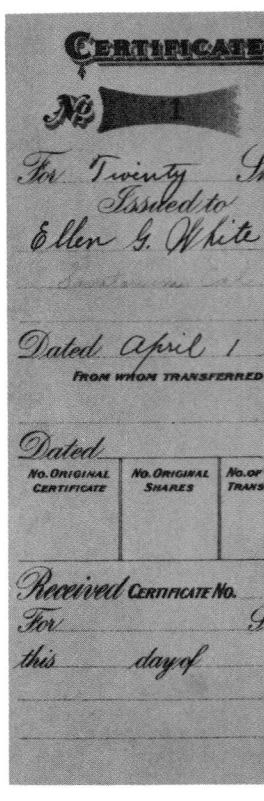

Dr. Whitelock and son, Thor

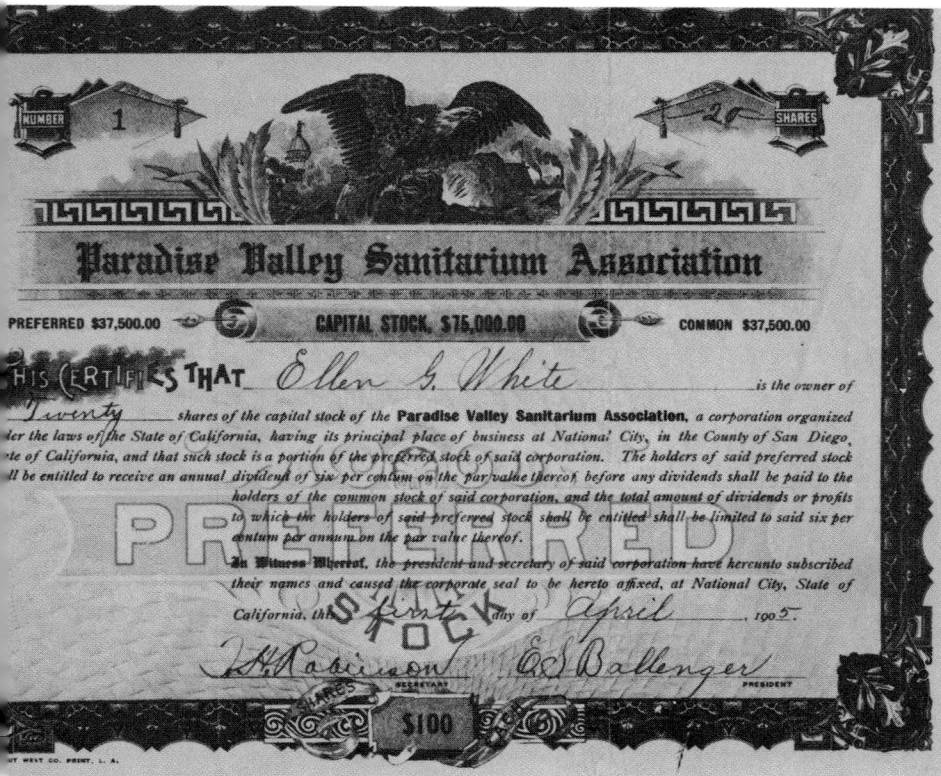

Ellen White purchased stock certificate No. 1, for twenty shares. As was usually the case, the lady from Elmshaven offered more than merely good counsel. She also raised money.

Dr. Anna M. Potts, the original owner, who was much gratified to see the institution again in operation. For more than a year, the sanitarium had been fully occupied by patients.

Despite its growth and development, the early years at the sanitarium required hard work and self-denial. A pioneer recalls those days:

"Paradise Valley Sanitarium was started in sacrifice and carried on in the same spirit, for we had few workers and much less money. Paydays were infrequent, and the salaries very small. The manager, when paid, received $7 per week. But as the climate was mild, cardboard served very well for repairing shoes. Earnest seasons of prayer were held daily for guidance, and these were answered in a very definite way, for our great interest was in our patients, and it was always held before us as workers that every patient that entered our door was sent by the Lord, and nothing must be left undone for his comfort.

"On the front grounds there was a beautiful fountain, and the pond lilies were much admired by the patients; but at night the frogs disturbed them, so the doctor, manager, matron, and all hands turned out to catch those cheerful little creatures.

"We might work in the operating room of the ladies' bath part of the day, and toward night paint the front porch, or wash the Turkish towels from the bath rooms. We had two stationary tubs and two washboards in the basement. That was our entire laundry equipment in those days. The only store was in a small adjoining room and was open one hour in the morning."

By the end of 1906, patronage at the sanitarium had grown so large that Dr. Whitelock recommended a sizeable addition to the main building. The trustees authorized this expansion, which was completed in 1907. The institution, now more than doubled in size, included new treatment and patient rooms and doctors' offices.

Also in 1906, the board reopened negotiations with the Southern California Conference of Seventh-day Adventists. Frequent changes were taking place in the executive and medical staffs of the institution. Prospective employees often asked, "Is the sanitarium a conference institution?" And moneylenders asked the same question. Loans were still needed, for, despite its growth, the sanitarium operated at a loss from 1906 to 1909. However, the board contrived an arrangement to transfer it to conference ownership, at a considerable sacrifice to the investors.

At the beginning of the new health institution the nurses lived in tents, as the sanitarium building had no rooms for nurses. These two are Helen and Zoe Horner.

When Ellen White heard of it, she strongly disapproved:

"I have received instruction from the Lord that the Paradise Valley Sanitarium should not be turned over to a new corporation organized by the conference; for to do this would be to act unjustly and unrighteously toward those who in good faith have invested their means in this enterprise. It is not just to place the valuation of the property at such a reduced figure. . . . The Lord has shown me that this property would better be retained by those who have put their means into it. He desires that those who, by their prayers and by the investment of their means, have shown their faith in this work, shall not be disappointed."

Some were disappointed by this counsel, but the operation continued as originally organized. Then the financial picture improved, and the sanitarium made sizable operating gains. Now the Southern California Conference changed its attitude and twice the conference committee voted to take over the sanitarium, finally doing so in 1912. The stockholders, who from the first considered that they were but holding the property in trust, relinquished their ownership, receiving back only their original investment without profit or interest. Henceforth, the conference owned and operated the Paradise Valley Sanitarium. At that time, there were only two hospitals in San Diego County—Mercy Hospital and Paradise Valley Sanitarium.

The aging little lady of Elmshaven, who had so strongly promoted the Paradise Valley project, never lost interest in it. Until her death in 1915, this selfless woman maintained a lively concern for its development. A frequent guest at the sanitarium, she remained for weeks at a time to enjoy rest and relaxation in the congenial surroundings she so obviously loved.

Above: Paradise Valley's first automobile, a Cadillac, brought guests from the railway station. The driver is William Payne (in the driver's seat at the right). In back is C. E. Rice, administrator from 1913 to 1916.

Left: Salem Hamilton, who lived to be ninety-nine, revisits the monument now standing on the site of the well he dug. Hamilton had accepted Adventism after hearing Ellen White preach in Nebraska. A poet, he expressed himself in unusual language—thus his statement about the Lord giving the "elephant" water to drink. As a youngster, his schoolteacher had threatened to punish him for misconduct, and Hamilton had composed an immediate reply: "I have a teacher/Her name is Miss Blodgett./She wants to hit me/But I'm going to dodge it!"

Below: Dr. A. D. Butterfield was medical director from 1919 to 1936.

Once established, Paradise Valley Sanitarium soon needed larger quarters.

Above: the sanitarium with an addition started in 1906 and completed the following year.

Left: Paradise Valley Sanitarium in 1934.

Below: the sanitarium's Medical Missionary Clinic also served as an evangelistic center. The sign at left announces the sermon topic, "Bootleggers—Will They Go to Heaven?" A most appropriate subject for those living only a few miles from the Mexican border!

WHAT MAKES BURDEN BORROW?

A TWENTY-DOLLAR BILL LAUNCHES ANOTHER HOSPITAL FOR THE LORD

f ever a man went knowingly, even joyfully, with his whole heart and his whole pocketbook into apparently hopeless debt, surely that man was John Allen Burden. He was not merely burdened with debt. He did not drift into debt or fall into it. He *marched* into debt, head held high, flags waving, bands playing. He was perhaps the only man who ever launched a major hospital with a twenty-dollar bill.

Ellen G. White had supported Elder A. G. Daniells, General Conference president, and other Adventist leaders in their purpose to avoid debt. Yet she recognized a danger in the extreme application of this principle. She wrote that the rule that "a sanitarium should not be established unless it could be started free of debt, has put the brake upon the wheels of progress." She referred to her own "experience in borrowing money and paying interest on it, to establish schools and sanitariums." She justified this course by the results—winning "many to the truth, thus increasing the tithe and adding workers to the Lord's forces."

Mrs. White had become well acquainted with the Saint Helena Sanitarium manager, John Burden, and had, as already mentioned, bought

the Elmshaven property from him. Burden seemed to her "a man of more than ordinary business acumen," but he was far more than that. Like Dr. David Paulson of Hinsdale, he had a special gift for deficit financing. The reason he took such great financial risks and succeeded was, of course, that he had implicit faith in God and His leading through the counsels of Ellen G. White.

The prophetess had declared, "A sanitarium should be established near Los Angeles. My brethren, will you not remember that it is the *expressed will of God* that this should be done?"

Burden had never, in the face of that kind of explicit instruction, learned how to doubt or delay. With orders from Heaven, he feared no failure. This extraordinary man was a key figure in the founding of both Glendale and Loma Linda Sanitariums; and, at different times, he managed three other principal medical centers, at Saint Helena, Paradise Valley, and Sydney, Australia.

Even before the Paradise Valley Sanitarium near San Diego was acquired in 1904, Mrs. White had urged the establishment of a sanitarium in the vicinity of Los Angeles. In 1901, about a year after her return from Australia, she wrote:

Spring Street in Los Angeles about 1880, at the time the first Seventh-day Adventists established themselves in that city. Two decades later, the prophetess declared, "A sanitarium should be established near Los Angeles. My brethren, will you not remember that it is the expressed will of God that this should be done?"

"On the night of October 10, 1901, I was unable to sleep after half past eleven. Many things regarding the sanitarium work were presented to me in signs and symbols. I was shown a sanitarium near Los Angeles in running order. . . . As in the visions of the night I saw this place, I said to our brethren, 'O, ye of little faith. You have lost much time.' On the lawn were the sick in wheelchairs. . . . There were many shade trees, the boughs of which hung down in such a way as to form leafy canopies. . . . Underneath these canopies were patients resting. The sick were delighted with their surroundings. While some worked, others were singing. There was no sign of dissatisfaction."

Two-and-a-half years later, on April 26, 1904, she sent another letter:

"Light has been given me that a sanitarium should be established near Los Angeles. . . . For years the need of such an institution has been kept before our people in Southern California. Had the brethren there heeded the warnings given by the Lord to guard them from making mistakes, they would not now be tied up as they are. But they have not followed the instruction given. They have not gone forward in faith to establish a sanitarium near Los Angeles."

Again, on June 30, 1904, Mrs. White wrote, describing the founding of a sanitarium near Los Angeles as "the expressed will of God," and urging:

"Why this work should be delayed from year to year is a great mystery. . . . Had the light given by God been followed, this institution might now be in running order, exerting a strong influence for good. Arrangements could have been made to utilize for sanitarium work buildings already erected."

In 1901, John Burden had gone to Australia; but upon his return three years later, Mrs. White persuaded him to look around the Los Angeles environs for a suitable sanitarium location. He found a number of deserted tourist and health resort buildings—mute evidences of the former land speculation. The one which appeared most suitable for sanitarium purposes was the huge, castle-like Glendale Hotel, built in 1886. It was located on a five-acre plot bordered by a rutty dirt road in what eventually became the 500 block of East Broadway. This seventy-five-room, unfurnished structure had cost $60,000. By the time it was completed, the nationwide depression of the early 1890's had struck California; and it never opened its doors as a hotel. Instead, for four years it was used as an Episcopal girls' school, St. Hilda's Hall. In 1901-1902, it served as a public high school until the first Glendale High School was built. Shade trees, orchards, chicken ranches, and a scattering of modest homes surrounded the property. By 1904, ownership had passed to Leslie C. Brand, a Glendale real estate developer, who was asking $26,000 for it.

The asking price was well beyond the financial limit given Mr. Burden, and he was discouraged. He decided, as he sat in the buggy looking over the hotel grounds, that if it could be obtained for $15,000, he would regard this as a sign of divine Approval. Taking several others with him, he approached Mr. Brand and said, "Our money will have to come from church members. Can you help us by reducing the price?" Mr. Burden's heart pounded. Mr. Brand thought a moment and then asked, "How does $12,500 sound?" Burden happily replied that it sounded fine, and eagerly signed an option. He drew a twenty-dollar bill from his pocket and gave it to Brand as earnest money.

The next day a new obstacle was encountered: The original deed had stipulated that this property should not become a sanitarium. However, the sympathetic Mr. Brand managed to get that clause deleted. A day after that, a second obstacle developed. The Conference lacked the $1,000 down payment. Mr. Burden then laid the matter before the constituency at the September, 1904, camp meeting. The constitutency rejected the purchase because there was no money in the treasury.

The hesitancy of the Southern California Conference leaders is understandable. With a membership of only about 1,100 and an indebtedness of nearly $40,000, it did not seem logical to plunge into new enterprises that would call for the expenditure of additional tens of thousands of borrowed dollars.

Unwilling to give up, Burden enlisted the help of Elder Clarence Santee, president of the conference. The two men decided to advance the money for the down payment out of their own pockets. At that crucial moment, Mrs. White sent them a message, and Santee read it to the conference delegates in session. She urged in the strongest terms that the purchase be made. "Why is this work delayed?" she again asked. She also persuaded two church members to advance $1,000 each for the down payment. Their enthusiasm stirred, the delegates quickly pledged $5,200 to buy the hotel. They made a cash payment of $4,500 and agreed to a three-year mort-

The original Glendale Sanitarium was the seventy-five-room Glendale Hotel building. Under construction in 1886, it opened just in time for a depression and became St. Hilda's Hall, an Episcopalian girls' school.

John Burden, left, Seventh-day Adventist sanitarium pioneer and manager, arranged the purchase of the old Glendale Hotel property with Leslie C. Brand, right, prominent developer of the city of Glendale.

gage for the balance. With this vote of confidence and support, the conference committee set up a board of trustees with Elder Santee as chairman and took immediate steps to refurbish and furnish the building.

Mrs. White was delighted. After visiting Glendale in December, 1904, she wrote:

"We feel grateful to God that our brethren and sisters in southern California have secured a property . . . which is well adapted for sanitarium purposes. . . . This new sanitarium is beautifully situated . . . in a pleasant valley. . . . It is in the country and yet can be very easily reached from the city, for an electric car line runs past the sanitarium grounds."

John Burden, persuaded to serve as manager of the new enterprise, at once sent out a call for volunteers. Unpaid workers eagerly responded and were soon wielding paintbrushes, mops, and brooms. They converted two rooms on the second floor into an operating room. Instruments, sheets and towels, dressings and sponges all had to be sterilized in a portable sterilizer on the kitchen stove. They painted packing boxes white and stacked them in the halls to serve as supply cupboards. They sponged every inch of the walls and floor with bichloride of mercury, a most effective method of sterilization.

With preparations complete and a staff and working force assembled, the Glendale Sanitarium opened its doors in August, 1905. In the absence of an admitting desk, the first medical director, Dr. Abbie Winegar Simpson, and the head nurse, Miss Lenora Lacey, greeted patients and guests at the door. Burden was too busy to greet guests on the opening day.

While the handicaps were many and the equipment crude, the sanitarium quickly earned an enviable reputation for "clean" cases, with a very low rate of infection. During the early years, the chief surgeon was Dr. Andrew S. Lobingier, a man of faultless surgery and excellent technique.

As the building had no elevators, all equipment and supplies, even water, had to be carried up and down the stairs by hand. Hydrotherapy treatments were usually given in the patient's room, where the water was heated in large tins on wood-burning stoves, each of the fifty patient rooms being thus furnished.

Guest rates, running from $16 to $25 per week, included room, board, regular medical treatments, and two hydrotherapy or physical therapy treatments a day. As late as 1924, a bill for a surgery patient shows the following: room and treatments, $2; operating room and anesthetic, $5; supplies and dressings, $1.50. Presumably, the surgeon's fee of $7.50 was billed separately.

But if the cost of service was low, so also was the pay of workers. Rates per hour for unskilled help ran from six to eight cents an hour while experienced persons, including nurses, earned eighteen to twenty cents an hour. Workers remained on duty sometimes for seemingly countless hours at a stretch. Japanese men servants did the room work, but there were no nurses on general duty. Neither was there a night clerk and, fortunately under the circumstances, no silent call service either. In case of dire necessity, a patient could ring his bell and sound a loud peal throughout the building. If this happened at night, the head nurse or matron would likely respond from her room on the floor above. If not, the black watchman, making the rounds of the building with lantern in hand, would eventually answer the call. But the nights were serenely quiet. No sound disturbed the prevailing tranquility after the last nightly street car rumbled past around 9:30.

With increasing patronage, the sanitarium prospered. The average patient stay during the first decade was between thirty and forty days. Visitors from as far away as the east coast came in such multiplying numbers to benefit from the life-giving treatments that in time it became almost impossible to get a room. Many liked the area so well that they made the sanitarium their temporary home while looking around for a place to live. Not infrequently they decided to remain in Glendale. Thus the institution developed into something more than a hospital and treatment center. John C. Sherer, in his *History of Glendale and Vicinity*, published in 1922, wrote:

Right: Mrs. Merrill, Glendale Sanitarium nurse in 1906, holds a baby by the name of McMurray. Below: nurses Naomi Carmichael Shaver and Mabel Hogue, 1911.

The Vision Bold

"It has upon many occasions been thrown open to the Glendale public for meetings of various kinds, requiring facilities for entertainment which no other place in the city could supply. The Chamber of Commerce has used its spacious dining room for more than one delightful banquet. . . . From which it will be apparent that the Glendale Sanitarium has filled a unique place in the life of Glendale and its rapid expansion in recent years, widely advertised as it has been, has been an important factor in making Glendale known to the outside world."

From the first, the sanitarium management saw the need for trained nurses, and set up a twenty-seven-month training program. The School of Nursing, inaugurated by Miss Lenora Lacey, accepted a transfer class that had been at the Adventist Los Angeles Treatment Rooms, and graduated its first class of two members in 1906.

The student nurse was on duty from twelve to twenty-four hours a day, and all special duty nursing was done by student nurses. Except for one-half day off on the Sabbath, no time off was provided. Nursing "probies" did all the chamber work, set up trays, waited tables, and worked in the laundry.

The student nurse's uniform consisted of a blue cambric dress, a white apron, and a ruffled cap. All dresses and uniforms had long sleeves, high bishop collars, ankle-length skirts, and high-topped black shoes. Corsets were forbidden, and all were required to wear their hair long.

Dr. Belle Wood Comstock became superintendent of nurses in 1910. With the support of Harmon Lindsay, business manager, and his wife Winifred, Dr. Comstock succeeded in getting the program accredited in 1911 by the California State Board of Nurse Examiners. At the beginning, nine grades of education were required for admission; but in 1911, applicants were required to have ten grades of education and be at least eighteen years old. Student nurses were allowed six, ten, and eighteen cents per hour for the three years, respectively.

By 1923, the population of Glendale had reached 30,000, and the Glendale Sanitarium had outgrown its facilities. A board committee was appointed to study the problem. Acting on the committee's recommendation, the trustees then voted to sell the old downtown property and to purchase for $50,000 a weed-infested thirty-acre plot—now 1509 Wilson Terrace—far out of town between the San Rafael foothills and the Sierra Madre range. Surrounded by apricot groves and unimproved land, the new site embraced a hill on the crest of which a new Glendale Sanitarium and Hospital was to be built. The old sanitarium property was sold for nearly $250,000.

Brand Boulevard, Glendale, in the 1920's.

Construction was begun without delay, but soon serious financial problems developed. The trustees had accepted a rough estimate of $500,000 for the cost of the new building. But as the project proceeded, costs escalated toward $800,000. The alarmed trustees referred the problem to the Pacific Union Conference Committee, who conferred with General Conference leaders in Washington, D.C. The men from Glendale and Washington made an excellent move. They agreed to set up a blue-ribbon committee with John A. Burden, former manager, as chairman to find their way out of the crisis.

So again, John Burden, the man who had so often successfully wrestled burdensome debts to the floor, took charge.

The Burden committee rendered a sensible, tactfully phrased report. Without placing explicit blame, it found the excessive costs to be due to many factors: (1) Inexperienced board members making decisions beyond the scope of their expertise; (2) unwise acceptance of hasty, ill-conceived cost estimates; (3) allowing material suppliers to add unwarranted percentages to their commissions; (4) employing union labor at excessive wages; (5) proceeding with construction without complete plans and specifications; (6) permitting frequent and excessive architectural changes during construction; (7) price increases of materials; (8) lack of coordination in scheduling the various construction services.

In making its report, the committee also pointed out that there had been a glaring want of clear-cut, overall responsibility assignments to the building superintendent, a failure to appoint a clerk of the works to approve the job in progress, and lack of an individual to keep track of inventories, equipment, and tools, which disappeared to the value of many thousands of dollars.

The Burden committee report recommended, among other things:

"Those who profit from their mistakes are truly wise.... Uniting believers with unbelievers in any association where the spirit of the unbelievers predominates is always dangerous to the work of God. Their influence counterworks that unselfish devotion and spirit of sacrifice that always has, and always will be, the first requisite of acceptable service in the work of God.

"There should be a marked contrast between the spirit and the motive of those who build for the work of God from the spirit of covetousness and self-seeking that characterize those that seek the highest wages and the shortest hours of labor.

"It is to be deeply regretted that the principles set forth in the building of the tabernacle in the wilderness were not followed . . . for the exercise of the spirit of self-denial and self-sacrifice is called for by the times before us. . . . God will bless His people as they unitedly move forward

In early Glendale Sanitarium days the city had abundant open spaces, but grew at a dizzying pace. Glendale Sanitarium was a recognized factor in the city's growth.

Architect's drawing of the new Glendale Sanitarium.

The building under construction.

The new Sanitarium opened its doors to patients on March 24, 1924.

revealing to the world the beauty of holiness as manifested in a Christlike spirit of self-sacrifice and in loving, untiring service for those in need of the blessings of the gospel."

The board of trustees was reorganized with J. J. Nethery as the new chairman. J. A. Burden was asked to serve again as manager for a time.

The General Conference granted substantial funds. Donations came in from constituents, and the remainder of the heavy debt was met by borrowing. Year after year, the management struggled with this inordinate obligation until, in the late 1930's, it was finally liquidated.

Despite its enormous cost, perhaps in part because of it, the new five-story, fireproof main

Glendale Sanitarium lobby in the late 1920's.

building was an impressive sight. The Spanish-type architecture and tile roof blended nicely with the environs. Inside could be found the latest in medical, surgical, and maternal facilities. When the surrounding acreage was attractively landscaped, the new institution became a lovely, restful place of curving drives, decorative shrubbery, well-cut lawns, and flowering trees.

By the spring of 1924, the new sanitarium was ready to open its doors to patients. Dedication services were held March 24, 1924, the twentieth anniversary of its founding, the main speaker being Elder A. G. Daniells, president of the General Conference of Seventh-day Adventists.

Another speaker, Administrator C. E. Kimlin, predicted that "in years to come the Glendale Sanitarium and Hospital will be in the middle of a great residential section as populous as all of Glendale today—and yet it will be forever on a hill; peaceful, serene, an institution of service and mercy to a fast-moving world below."

Now renamed "Glendale Adventist Hospital," it is there on the hill today because God Himself, through His spokeswoman at Elmshaven, declared that it should be done. And it is there because John Burden, the "man of more than ordinary business acumen," heeded that voice and handed Mr. Brand his twenty-dollar bill.

PRESENT AT THE PURCHASE OF GLENDALE SANITARIUM
Ernest Lloyd Remembers

Ernest Lloyd, an errand boy for John Harvey Kellogg in the 1890's, still lives. Now ninety-five, he is spry and active and eager to share his remarkable store of memories. Lloyd was also acquainted with Ellen White, Will Kellogg, David Paulson, and many of the young medics recruited and trained at Battle Creek who later manned the sanitariums in the West.

After his five years at Battle Creek, Lloyd moved to southern California. He actually accompanied John A. Burden on the visit to Leslie C. Brand when Burden made the down payment to purchase Glendale Sanitarium. Lloyd became a minister, a conference colporteur leader, and later a writer and editor. He now lives at Deer Park, California, near the foot of Howell Mountain overlooking Elmshaven.

In a recent interview, Elder Lloyd reminisced:

I was born in Guelph, Ontario, and my parents moved to Chicago three years afterward. When I was seventeen, I went to Battle Creek to attend the college. That was the fall of 1896, and I stayed there five years, till 1901. I got a job at the sanitarium as one of eighteen or twenty errand boys or "runners." We were all over town, and this was important, for sometimes the old telephone system would be out of commission.

Who were some of the other young people working there?

One was Harry Miller, who became the famous "China Doctor." He started hospitals in the Orient and performed goiter operations and invented health foods. George Thomason, who later became a great surgeon, also worked for Kellogg, but not as a runner. He and Arthur Spalding had taken stenography—you know, shorthand. They served the doctor at night only. No one ever saw the doctor dictate a letter during the day. He was too busy. So these men would come out to his home in the evening. They'd have a couple of typewriters, and one would take notes in his book, then go and transcribe while the other was taking more letters from Dr. Kellogg. The doctor never stood or sat while dictating. He always lay down on a couch, relaxed.

Did you personally see him that way?

Oh, yes. And I never heard a man talk faster than Dr. Kellogg when dictating.

I suppose he stayed in high gear most of the time.

Yes, in very high gear.

He was a man of many talents.

Yes, the man was a genius. He learned the printing business at the age of twelve, did proofreading at the age of fourteen, and at

sixteen was a public schoolteacher. The next year, he attended high school for one year and graduated. By the time he was twenty-two, James White made him editor of the *Health Reformer*. Remarkable!

Yes, they don't give top editorial positions to people that young today.

By the way, did you ever hear how Ellen White saved Kellogg's life when he was ten years of age? She thought he looked pale, as if he might get tuberculosis, so she invited him into the Whites' home for about six months. Sister White at this time was taking exercises for herself in the backyard after breakfast, and the boy went right into that program. I've heard him speak of this in one of his lectures. So Kellogg kept up the exercising and deep breathing all through his life. As a famous doctor he had a little program of his own when he awakened from his sleep. He would go out to his track to run for awhile. The Kellogg home occupied a block and the large three-story house was in one corner. The block was fenced in very nicely, and just inside the fence was a path all around the block. He'd run so many laps, forget just how many. They would vary with the days, maybe a half-mile, maybe a mile.

He would walk?

He would run—jog.

You've seen him running?

Oh, yes, many times. He was a short man, a little shorter than I am, and a "live wire." Then he'd run into the house, into the bathroom, take his cold-mitten friction and dress and come to breakfast, and be off to the hospital. He did his surgical work in the early morning. That was his habit.

Did you meet any of the famous guests at the Battle Creek Sanitarium?

Once I was in one of the hydrotherapy rooms, and I heard one of the bath boys sing out, "Three hundred and twelve pounds." A portly gentleman had just had some treatments to try to reduce his weight, and he had stepped on the scales. He was a senator from Ohio who later became President William Howard Taft. He would lose weight on his visits to Battle Creek, then go home and gain back the weight.

Did you know Will Kellogg? What do you remember most about him?

I knew him very well. I was his office boy one summer. He was a hardheaded businessman with a soft heart, but not everyone knew how softhearted he was. Some of us boys who carried little sealed notes from him to certain widows around the town—we knew

I especially remember two cases, and I knew there were checks in those envelopes to cover two mortgages. But these women were sworn to silence; they were not to talk to anybody about it.

What else do you remember about W. K.?

In the summer of 1900, he did something for me and another boy, Dave Ferguson. We had been student colporteurs. I spent my summers in Iowa among the farmers, and I've always felt grateful to the farmers of Iowa for helping to get me through school. Well, here comes 1900, and about a month before school closed, he called Dave and Ernest into his office. He said, "I want to talk to you boys about a little idea that I have to increase our patronage and also to keep in touch with old friends and patients down in the state of Texas." He went on to tell us his plan:

"We'd like to have you two boys go down to Texas and start in at Fort Worth. You'll arrive on a Thursday night and you'll run out to Cleburne to spend the Sabbath. We'll write to Professor C. C. Lewis and his wife—they have charge of the school—and you can stay there Sabbath. Then back to Fort Worth and on about your work. We'll supply you with the names of former patients from Fort Worth, Dallas, Waco, Austin, San Antonio, Houston, Galveston—the big cities. You'll find quantities of booklets in the express offices in each city waiting for you, also boxes of our latest health foods—little samples. You'll go to the homes of our old patients and tell them who you are and where you come from.

"So you'll knock on the door," he told us, "and tell the lady of the house your names. Tell them you are from Battle Creek, and Dr. Kellogg and the business manager, Will Kellogg, sent you. Tell her we are happy to send our greetings and also to give her a package of our health food and this booklet with new pictures. And after a little visit—don't stay too long—she'll have some questions, of course. When you are about to leave, you ask if she has any relative or friend in the city who should go to Battle Creek for help, for treatment." Usually, we'd get an affirmative answer, and so we'd get the address, you see.

So you contacted more patients for the sanitarium and promoted the health foods in the same visit.

Exactly. You get the picture. When the people gave us names of people to visit, we went to see them right then, before we left town.

Was W. K. pleased with your work? Did the visits get results?

Yes, when we got home in the fall, W. K. showed us letters that had come in. People wanted more information, and some had asked for reservations at the sanitarium.

Did you know Charles W. Post?

When I arrived in 1896, Post was already starting up his business. But I knew the background story. The Kelloggs had him at reduced rates as a sanitarium patient. Well, he began to recover after some weeks. As he regained his strength, he went over to our little old food factory, the *first health food factory in America*, a little wooden building. Sometimes we boys would help over there. Post was interested in the granola—ground up crackers and so on—and also in our caramel cereal, which was a coffee substitute. Well, he was in and out, and as the days went by people began to report all of this to Dr. Kellogg. "That's all right. Just leave him alone," Kellogg said. So as soon as Post was back on his feet again, he left the sanitarium and put up a little wooden building. Pretty soon he was making Postum.

Some of the people said to Dr. Kellogg, "You ought to sue that man."

"Oh, no, nothing like that. The more people we can get away from coffee the better, my friend." See, Dr. Kellogg was always thinking *education*. Within two years, Post was a millionaire. He was a good advertiser.

Did you know Dr. David Paulson very well?

Well, I should say so! He was one of the finest Christians, one of the most marvelous men we ever had. Dr. Paulson and Dr. Daniel H. Kress and Dr. Howard F. Rand were, I would say, Dr. Kellogg's three best aides in the medical work in the institution. We had others.

At first, I was a regular call boy in the institution, and then I was promoted. We were taught all sorts of things. We call boys had to take a little course, covering a period of about three months. We learned how to fix up an ice bag, even how to give a fomentation to the spine—lots of things about the care of patients. Besides, they taught us to wash dishes and pots and pans. In the basement, under the regular kitchen where we washed the pots and pans, they had a dumbwaiter. I was working there one day, and here comes Dr. Paulson. I was surprised. He came over to where I stood.

"Well, Ernest, do you know that you are standing right where I stood years ago and washed pots and pans? Ernest, this work is just exactly as important as my work upstairs as a medical man or Dr. Kellogg's or anyone else's. If these things are not properly washed and cared for, we're going to have trouble."

Well, I knew that, but a little tonic, a little encouragement was helpful.

Did you ever visit Dr. Paulson's missions in Chicago?

I was right there for three months.

Did you work with him in the clinics?

Yes, the boys were taken over there at different times. We helped bring in drunks. We were at the Working Men's Home and the Life Boat Mission. Dr. Paulson started the *Life Boat* magazine, and we all had to get out occasionally and sell magazines. A boy by the name of Rochambeau—he later became a lawyer in Glendale—and another boy and I, the three of us sold the first 500 copies of *Life Boat*.

Did you meet Ellen White in Battle Creek?

Only once in Battle Creek. But I came to California in 1904, and between 1904 and 1915 we often met her at camp meetings, Pacific Press meetings, and at Elmshaven.

Did you have personal conversations with her?

A few short ones. Of course, she was a very busy woman. She was an inspired prophetess of God—there's no doubt about it.

Now let's shift over to southern California. Please tell us about the beginnings of Glendale Sanitarium.

I was looking after the colporteur work. I had done pretty well with the book work, so Elder Clarence Santee, our first president in southern California, put me to work looking after this department. I got acquainted with Elder Burden, and we made some calls together on some of our members. He said to me, "You know a lot of our people in our churches, and some of them have money. So you can help us."

Elder Burden and I got an appointment with Mr. Brand, a big man in Glendale. We took with us Mr. and Mrs. Learned and Chaplain Marvin, some of our members in Glendale. We went to Brand's office; and he invited us in. We sat down and Brother Burden talked about the big hotel that failed in the crash. It was down the street a little from Mr. Brand's office. It had been a girls' school for the Episcopalians and was now closed.

"What do you people want the building for?" Mr. Brand asked.

"We're thinking of starting a branch sanitarium out here," Burden told him.

"A branch sanitarium?"

"Yes," Burden went on, "similar to the famous Battle Creek Sanitarium, with hydrotherapy treatments and healthful diets, and all the rest."

"I know Battle Creek," Mr. Brand said. He asked some questions about Battle Creek, and I was able to answer them, knowing that city as I did.

"Well," he decided, "that sounds good to me. That would be a good thing for this little town. This town is going to grow up to be a city." Then he said, "The price of that hotel up there is $26,000. Now, if you can produce a sanitarium similar to Battle Creek, you can have it for $12,500."

So Burden opened his pocketbook and took out a twenty-dollar bill and handed it to Mr. Brand as the first payment. I can see him now.

LOMA LINDA

JOHN BURDEN'S ROLLTOP DESK

THE RESURRECTION OF LONESOME LINDA

A New Medical Center Gets Off to a Very Shaky Start

"Lonesome Linda" they called her—the hulking wooden hotel on the hill. She was one of those grandiose gingerbread structures that dotted the southern California landscape following the boom and bust of the 1880's. Revived in the nineties, she faltered again, and her owners reluctantly hung the "for sale" sign on her.

Soon after the Civil War, thousands had begun to flock westward as news spread of California's healthful climate and rich farmlands. The flow of immigrants to California reached its peak in the 1880's; and southern California, especially, found itself in a major real-estate bonanza. A rate war between the Southern Pacific and the Santa Fe railroads added more steam to the boilers. The competing lines actually sold some tickets for as little as *one dollar*, for transportation from the Midwest to Los Angeles. Because many immigrants were health seekers, especially those afflicted with throat and lung diseases, real estate developers built sanitariums and hotel-type structures to accommodate the expected demand.

The land grab reached its peak in 1888, then fell off sharply. People left Los Angeles at the rate of a thousand a month. Vaunted towns and villas, with their "come-on" hotels and sanitariums, stood stark in the midst of half-developed or undeveloped tracts. A few of these institutions survived as intended by their promoters, but others sank into a morass of legal tangles. Many of them, "Ichabod" written over their doorways, stood forlorn and empty except for bats and visiting vandals.

The tiny Seventh-day Adventist churches of southern California had already acquired two of these bargain-basement properties — Paradise Valley and Glendale — and were struggling to develop, furnish, and pay for them. Now, amazingly, Ellen White, still not satisfied, was talking of a third! There must be, she said, still another occupied site with buildings away from the city, suitable for a sanitarium. In December, 1904, she traveled by rail through Loma Linda three times within a week. She may have seen the name "Loma Linda" on the Southern Pacific station, and perhaps she caught a glimpse of the front elevation of Loma Linda Hotel. She did not, however, detrain and inspect the property. The whole of the citrus belt from Redlands to Riverside impressed her as a most desirable area.

Three times in early 1905, Ellen White urged a search for property in this area. Finally, she told John A. Burden and his committee that a suitable

175

site could be found near Redlands. This no doubt brought to their minds the Loma Linda property which they had discovered in March of the previous year.

First developed as Mound City, with its Mound City Hotel, this tourist center failed with the crash of 1888, which lasted until the nationwide depression of 1893. When business recovered in the late nineties, new owners, including a large number of Los Angeles physicians, changed the name of the property to Loma Linda and attempted to turn the institution into a fine health resort. This also failed, and the neighbors nicknamed her "Lonesome Linda."

Burden and his committee remembered the fully furnished, beautiful hotel building with an amusement center, five cottages, a farmhouse with implements, horses, carriages, and cows on a seventy-six acre tract. They remembered the eighteen acres of bearing orchard and fifteen in alfalfa. But they dared not contemplate the quoted price of $110,000. Mrs. White's wisdom, nevertheless, seemed to point toward Loma Linda.

When Burden renewed the contact, the owners quoted a price of $85,000. Soon afterward they shrank the asking price to $45,000. When Mrs. White stopped briefly in Los Angeles in early May, on her way to a General Conference session in Washington, D.C., Burden told her about the spectacular bargain. At once enthusiastic, she advised further investigation, the results to be reported to her in Washington.

Two days later, Elder Burden and his committee revisited Loma Linda, and discreet negotiation resulted in a firm price of $40,000. Burden reported in detail by mail to Ellen White on the same day, suggesting that she take up the matter with the brethren in conference. The first paragraph of Mrs. White's reply of May 14 contained a shocker for one used to getting committee clearance before making important moves:

"Your letter has just been read. I had no sooner finished reading it than I said, 'I will consult no one; for I have no question at all about the matter.' I advised Willie [her son] to send you a telegram without spending time to ask the advice of the brethren. Secure the property by all means, so that it can be held, and then obtain all the money you can and make sufficient payments to hold the place. This is the very property we ought to have. Do not delay; for it is just what is needed. . . . We will do our utmost to help you raise the money."

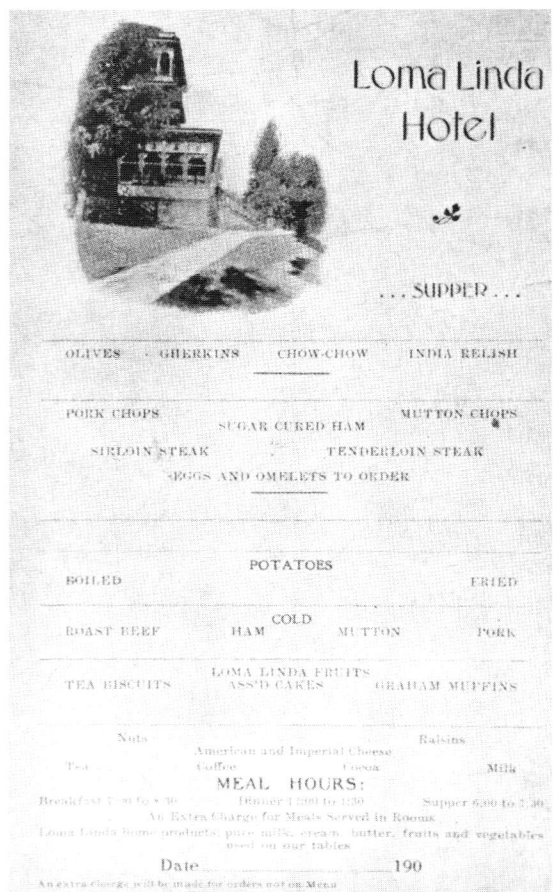

Early Loma Linda Hotel menus were no foretaste of things to come later. One menu offered guests a choice of pork chops, mutton chops, sugar-cured ham, sirloin steak, tenderloin steak, and eggs and omelets to order, besides cold meat and tea and coffee. A few items seem most appropriate—"Loma Linda fruits" and "graham muffins."

On receipt of this letter, Burden and others tried to raise money among the few church members known to be somewhat prosperous; but these had given freely for the purchase, remodeling, and equipping of the two other sanitariums.

Members of the conference committee who did not go to Washington felt that Mrs. White should have consulted the brethren before giving Burden such specific instruction. To keep themselves in the clear, they wired their colleagues in Washington, who promptly replied that they would "take no responsibility in the matter." Because Mrs. White continued writing letters urging that the property be secured, Burden and his remnant committee found themselves in deep perplexity. Several wires were sent to Washington. When an answer came, both Ellen White and the committee members in Washington had signed it. They requested delay of the matter until they returned to California.

The owners refused to extend the option to buy the property, which had only a few days to run. Elder Burden secured from the owners a promise to give an option to hold the property until June 15, on payment of $1,000. On fulfillment of the terms of the option on June 15, an additional payment of $4,000 would be due to complete the first installment of $5,000.

The immediate question was where to get the earnest money of $1,000 to bind the escrow. Another letter from Ellen White about this time stated that if they would move forward, money would come from unexpected sources. Since no money seemed to be in sight, their problem was where they should look.

A friend of Burden's, Elder R. S. Owen of San Fernando, recalled having heard a man say that if and when he could sell some property he would make the proceeds available to a good cause. Thursday afternoon, May 25, Burden and Owen took an interurban line toward the man's farm south of Los Angeles. From a crossing they walked a mile and a half or more to the farmhouse, finding no one at home. They returned to the rail line, but for some unknown reason failed to flag the car. Having over two hours to wait, they chanced another walk in the dusk back to the farm. They saw a light in the house, and found the family eating their evening meal. Calling the farmer by name (which now seems to be unknown), the two men introduced themselves, acknowledging that they had never met before. Burden broke the ice by asking the farmer if he knew Ellen White.

"Yes," he replied, and his interest picked up immediately. Encouraged, Burden pulled from his pocket recent letters from Mrs. White, reading from them and making explanations as necessary to clarify the story.

The man warmed to the occasion. Burden came straight to the point, declaring his understanding that his new-found friend had some money with which he might help them.

"Praise the Lord," responded the farmer, throwing down his knife and fork in a gesture of enthusiasm not commonly manifest by men being asked for heavy donations. "Why, I have been praying for months for the Lord to send us a buyer."

They had recently sold out, and had the money lying in the bank. Burden and Owen were filled with joy and thanksgiving when the man pulled from his pocket "a bank deposit check for $2,400," which he signed over to Burden. No one had a receipt form; the benefactor said none was called for. He added, "The Lord is in this; it is all right." Burden's faith was fortified for trials yet to come.

The option was scheduled to terminate the next day, May 26. Early that morning Burden notified the owners by phone that the purchasers were ready to do business. The two parties and their lawyers met in early afternoon and began the business of drawing up the papers. This was Friday and time was not sufficient to list all the chattels, so they agreed to complete the task on Monday morning.

Meanwhile, the members of the local committee in Washington consulted the Pacific Union Conference Committee. Saturday evening a wire brought their new decision: *"Developments do not warrant securing Loma Linda."*

Burden now must have feared that he was setting the stage for a confrontation between Ellen White, spiritual guide and leader of the church, and the elected California leaders and their supporters. Burden knew, too, that the recently elected president of the Southern California Conference had been given a mandate to get the conference out of debt. Perhaps Burden recalled that the purchase of Paradise Valley and Glendale Sanitariums were both initiated by private enterprise. Being an establishment man by nature, yet an ardent believer in Ellen White's gift of divine inspiration, Burden decided to sign the papers as an individual and not as representative of an organization. Thus, he took the personal chance of losing the $1,000 he promised to the owners. Mrs. Burden joined with him in this act of faith.

Burden delivered the $1,000 Monday morning, May 29, and signed the papers. Within a few days, Mrs. White's letter dated May 24 arrived. It was in part foreboding:

"We received your letter today. I wish to say I cannot ask the conference to invest in a sanitarium at Redlands [Loma Linda]. They have enough responsibilities."

This news was anything but comforting to the hard-pressed John Burden. A letter written shortly afterward proved more encouraging. On May 31, Mrs. White wrote: "We hope to see you soon now, but in regard to the purchasing of

'Loma Linda,' I can do no more except to borrow. I wish the place purchased. Do not neglect to tell me all I ought to know. I have been looking over your descriptive letter, and I am well satisfied that the place is one we ought to have. It is cheap at forty thousand dollars. We will not leave you, but will stand back of you and help you raise the means. In regard to the right men to manage the institution, I am confident that we shall find someone when the right time comes."

While Ellen White was writing this, Burden wrote her a long letter urging her to return home by way of Los Angeles to help in planning for the immediate future. The additional $4,000 due June 15 loomed large in the mind of the man who had signed the sales contract. Further, $5,000 would be due on July 26, $5,000 on August 26, and $5,000 more by January 1, 1906. The balance then would be secured by a three-year mortgage on the property. Burden was convinced that Mrs. White's presence and a favorable action by the conference before June 15 would bring success.

Why did so many church officials resist the Loma Linda venture? The church had already engaged in extensive programs of building, staffing, and operating colleges, schools, hospitals, publishing houses, and church buildings at home and abroad. Because activated plans often exceeded available funds, debts accumulated at a rapid rate in many places. Even Ellen White became much concerned and counseled responsible officials to shun debt like leprosy. Curtailment and delay were often the price of avoiding debt. Ellen White was frequently concerned with long-range objectives, while elected officials often had to act in the light of immediate facts. Hence, their value judgments were at times contrary.

Another overarching influence was the aftermath of the virtual schism resulting from the organizational feud between Elder Arthur G. Daniells, president of the General Conference, and Dr. John H. Kellogg, medical director of the Battle Creek Sanitarium and president of the American Medical Missionary College. As a result, the General Conference withdrew from its organizational association with the Sanitarium and College. When Kellogg was accused of teaching pantheism in a recently published book, *The Living Temple,* the clergy of the church were strongly inclined to write off Dr. Kellogg as a purveyor of heresy. The majority of medical men within the church were less critical of Dr. Kellogg. Some doubted that Kellogg had really departed from orthodoxy; all continued to respect him professionally.

As a result of this struggle, a thin veil of prejudice and distrust tended to separate the ministerial and medical brethren. The former were tied theologically and economically to the church establishment; the latter, by the very nature of their profession, sensed a degree of independence. Both groups had tended to suppress the problem into the subconscious, but at times circumstances conspired to force it to the surface, thereby often confusing an issue not directly related to the original conflict. Such agitations have been referred to flippantly as the Battle Creek syndrome or Battle Creek phobia. The Loma Linda project in 1905 seems to have suffered the delaying impact of this phenomenon. The cause was still fresh in everybody's mind, but not freely acknowledged or perhaps even recognized.

After the return of the committee members from Washington, a meeting was called for Sunday, June 11. Because Loma Linda was the urgent item on the agenda, the leaders asked John Burden for a report. His own brief reminiscence of the meeting reveals little of the charged atmosphere which must have pervaded this session. Burden merely reported what he had done. "Naturally," he wrote years later, "some of the committee felt that . . . we had acted unadvisedly," and one member suggested that they "must officially repudiate all responsibility for what had been done."

Tension lessened when it was made clear that the purchase was not consummated in the name of the conference. Supporters of the purchase then urged all members to attend a council meeting with Mrs. White at Loma Linda the next morning before taking any action. After some hesitation, the reluctant members agreed. With them went about twenty-five members of the Los Angeles church.

Soon after ten o'clock Monday morning, the members from Los Angeles were inspecting the grounds and buildings when Ellen White and her group arrived in an express wagon from the Redlands station. Transcontinental trains made no stops at Loma Linda.

As Ellen White alighted, she said to her son, W. C. White, "Willie, I have been here before."

He replied, "No, Mother, you have never been here."

"Then this is the very place the Lord has shown me," she insisted, "for it is all familiar."

John Allen Burden (1862-1942), the man Mrs. White described as "of more than ordinary business acumen," was a key figure in acquiring the Glendale and Loma Linda properties. At the age of twenty-nine, he became manager of Rural Health Retreat at Saint Helena, and later served as manager at Sydney, Glendale, Loma Linda, and Paradise Valley.

Turning to a bystander she added, "We must have this place. We should reason from cause to effect. The Lord has not given us this property for any common purpose."

This introductory dialogue was well timed for the doubting Thomases in the group. As Mrs. White walked around the grounds, she repeated, "This is the very place the Lord has shown me." As they entered the assembly building, she spoke prophetically:

"This building will be of great value to us. A school will be established here. Redlands will become a center as also will Loma Linda. Battle Creek is going down. God will reestablish His medical work at this place."

The group in Loma Linda reached no decision on June 12, with only three days to go. A larger council was called for ten o'clock the next day in the Carr Street Church in Los Angeles. Those present voted unanimously to purchase Loma Linda and open it as a sanitarium. Conference officials, however, would not act on the recommendation of only one congregation. They agreed that a selected group should accompany Mrs. White the next day to San Diego to present the matter to the members there and later call a meeting of delegates from all the churches in the conference on June 20. The San Diego group voted that the conference "should bear no responsibility in the matter."

The June 20 meeting took place five days after the due date of June 15. The fact that members of the conference committee at the Carr Street meeting had implied that they would assume the responsibility if the delegates on June 20 would authorize it sounded favorable. Thus encouraged, fund raisers began work. Three persons guaranteed $3,000. A total of $4,400 was then available to pay the $4,000 due on June 15.

One church opposed to incurring additional debt sent no delegates to the June 20 conference session. Elder Burden described the property, and the conference president spoke of the financial involvement. Then came Mrs. White's address and earnest appeal in favor of the purchase. San Diego delegates urged that the property be privately owned as was the Paradise Valley Sanitarium, which had not yet been taken over by the conference. Elder G. A. Irwin, a vice-president of the General Conference, made a plea for conference participation which turned the tide of opinion and loosened purse strings.

As soon as Elder Irwin was seated, the daughter of General Harrison Gray Otis, founder of the Los Angeles *Times*, arose and addressed the audience. She declared that she favored the purchase and would give $10,000 if and when she could get the sum released from its present commitment. Her boldness inspired the audience. They soon voted overwhelmingly that the Southern California Conference should purchase Loma Linda. Eleven hundred dollars in cash and pledges were raised before adjournment.

Another test of faith followed soon after. Because the hesitancy of certain conference officials had become common knowledge, those with means still balked at providing funds for the next $5,000 payment due in three weeks. Burden, who had raised money for the Saint Helena Sanitarium in the churches of the San Joaquin and Sacramento Valleys, went north with a request to the California Conference to solicit funds for Loma Linda. The request was denied because the Pacific Union Conference had advised the Southern California Conference in May not to invest in any more sanitariums. When the day arrived, the treasury contained only a small sum.

Suspense reigned when the committee went into session that morning. The leading officers recommended that they acknowledge their inability to follow through and "lose the five thousand dollars already paid if necessary and be freed from further obligation." Those who so far had borne the burden of the purchase firmly resisted the suggestion. When pressed by the committee to offer a solution, they could only answer in faith that somehow the Lord would bring relief, and suggested that possibly the morning mail would bring the answer.

Just then they heard the mailman's tread as he ascended the stairs to their second-floor office. The room was quiet; they nearly choked with hope and anxiety as the carrier took the last few steps. He delivered a letter postmarked Atlantic City, New Jersey. Who could have sent it? No one knew until it was opened. It enclosed a draft for $5,000!

As each looked at the other, all eyes flooded with tears. Deeply moved, the chief opponent broke the silence. "It seems that the Lord is in this thing," he said.

There was a quick answer: "Of course He is, and He is going to carry it through." The donor had been told of the need by Ellen White.

John Burden and his associates began canvassing the churches in the Southern California Conference in anticipation of the third $5,000 payment. They obtained nothing, but time still remained. Then a letter came from a member in Oregon who had heard of the purchase. He asked if any money was needed and received a prompt reply. His check for $4,500 arrived in time. To it they added the $400 left over from the original gift. Then a woman encouraged by the acts of faith by others gave the last $100 needed for the payment.

Soon sufficient money came in to make the fourth payment before it was due. In recognition of this courtesy, the sellers reduced the balance by $100. About this time, the sellers discovered that they could not distribute to their stockholders the $20,000 paid until their corporation was ready to be dissolved. Dissolution could not be legally effected until they received payment of the three-year note. Anxious for their money, the stockholders authorized a discount of $1,000 on the balance of $20,000. The new owners began a search for $18,900.

Meanwhile, Loma Linda Sanitarium received its first guest. The institution was not quite prepared for guests, but this one was made comfortable. On her second day, she wandered through the beautiful grounds. Recently widowed, she felt sad and tearful. 'I get so lonesome,' she confided to Elder Burden, "that sometimes I wish I were dead." She thought she could be happy living in such a place, so someone suggested a life annuity. She was ushered to the business office. When a cash payment of $7,000 was quoted, she brightened and said: "Why, I have that much in cash." Both parties signed the contract. She paid $6,200 by December 18 and promised the balance by February 1. She became a guest of the institution, but was not thought of as a patient.

An elderly brother in the church arranged for a similar annuity for $3,500. When a former Glendale patient learned of the discount offered for a final settlement, she offered to lend $15,000 for two or three years. Thus within seven months a total of $38,900—some as gifts and some as loans—had come in, and payment was made in full.

"The entrance steps broaden as one ascends, and from them is entered the glass parlor."
—Ellen G. White.

The Resurrection of Lonesome Linda

"We have recently purchased another sanitarium property, known as Loma Linda. I am most grateful to the Lord for making it possible to secure this property. It lies sixty miles east of Los Angeles, on the main line of the Southern Pacific Railway. Its name, Loma Linda, —'Beautiful Hill'—describes the place."—E. G. W.

The conflict of personalities that threatened to disrupt the Loma Linda acquisition in the first three or four months had been unpleasant. In the end, however, true Christian brothers had the capacity to forgive and adjust.

The new owners occupied Loma Linda on July 1. When Ellen White visited the new institution in late August, she enthusiastically reported:

"In the cellar I see a large quantity of jellies that have been put up. Shelf after shelf is laden with jars of rich fruit. . . . Some of the fruit will be sent to the Sanitarium at San Diego."

A group of workers began on October 1 preparing for the reception of patients. On the ninth, John Burden wrote to Ellen White: "Dr. G. K. Abbott is with us, and a number of other workers." Also, "Loma Linda is now open to receive patients." The first patient was registered on October 12. However, Burden considered that the Sanitarium did not officially open until November 1, and dated his financial statements accordingly.

The shortage of operating capital presented a gloomy picture. The manager gave applicants for work no assurance when salaries could be paid. He invited them, nevertheless, to come and share in the poverty, receiving only board and room. Thirty-five people had reported for duty by November 1. On December 18, there were twenty-five patients. Burden predicted that soon he would be meeting all expenses including wages. At the end of the first fiscal year of eight months, the balance sheet showed a gain of $1,160.22; the second year (twelve months) showed $1,751.24. Extensive subsidies made these balances possible.

Dr. Julia White, the first superintendent of nurses, arrived in late November, 1905, and initiated plans for nursing education. Early in 1906, Elder and Mrs. S. N. Haskell arrived to teach and sponsor evangelistic activities. It was widely rumored, if not generally understood, that the education of physicians was to be a part of the program, but no one understood clearly the *modus operandi* of such a program.

A council of Pacific Union Conference and Southern California Conference officials met at Loma Linda in April, 1906, and agreed to name the institution "Loma Linda College of Evangelists." Ellen White delivered the dedicatory address on April 15. With the sanitarium in satisfactory beginning operation, the council devoted itself to the educational program. Warren E. Howell, an experienced educator, was called to be the first president and John A. Burden was recognized as business manager.

Mrs. White addressed the group, laying emphasis on the future educational program. Her use of the words "gospel medical missionary evangelists" was not interpreted in terms of curriculum organization. The first prospectus of Loma Linda College of Evangelists gave some insight into the meaning of the four words:

"By the term 'evangelists' is not necessarily meant a popular lecturer or preacher on gospel themes, or a general revivalist, as is commonly understood, but rather a teacher of the original gospel in its simplicity and purity, as it pertains to the physical, the intellectual, and the spiritual welfare of the individual, whether the teaching be done by what is ordinarily called the teacher, the preacher, the physician, the Bible worker, or the colporteur."

The first prospectus, brought out in the summer of 1906, listed four courses including "Evangelistic-Medical Course." It seemed to be intended as a continuing course for graduate nurses and others with high school diplomas. It was not a medical course *per se*. Concerned over the demand for a course leading toward the M.D. degree, President Howell called on Ellen White at Saint Helena. She repeated her general guidelines and added: "We cannot mark out a precise line to be followed unconditionally."

The opening of the school year was set for September 20, 1906. At the appointed time, part of the faculty assembled and conducted devotional exercises, but no students had arrived. By October 4, with thirty-five students and all the faculty present, school started.

The big question among students was, would the school be accredited? Prospective medical students busied themselves with various courses, but wanted to know if they were wasting their time. The trustees and church officials felt concern, but avoided a forthright answer to the question of a medical school. There was much talk but uncertain leadership for the time. Should the college attempt to educate regular physicians, or should they present to the public a new breed of healers who, like osteopaths or chiropractors, would operate under their own board, licensing them to practice in the state?

President Howell, having had no experience in medical education, resigned before the close of the first year. Burden felt that Howell would not "throw his interest into the medical work." More likely, Howell considered his appointment incompatible with his sense of academic integrity, which prohibited his claiming professional competence in an area unknown to him.

Of necessity, John Burden, who was board chairman as well as business manager, exercised some of the functions of the president until the election of Dr. George K. Abbott to fill the vacancy left by Professor Howell. Burden's letter of February 3 to W. C. White expressed his regret at Howell's decision. He asked Elder White to counsel with his mother about the medical school problem. Two months later, he addressed himself to several church leaders. He reported that most of the prospective medical students had enrolled in the nursing course (1906-07), which would not be satisfactory to them for another year.

Of necessity, a medical council convened in Loma Linda on October 28-31, 1907. One hundred people, including numerous church leaders, were present. They passed fifteen resolutions, some with desirable substance, others only pious declarations. Not one of the resolutions answered the basic curriculum problem, though some actions did stimulate a move which culminated two years later in securing for the college a charter which listed medical and dental schools.

Mrs. White was present at this council, and Burden quizzed her publicly. Was the college "to embrace also the qualifications for physicians?"

She replied: "Physicians are to receive their education here." Seemingly, Ellen White knew

"At the right of the hall, double doors open into a large dining room." — E. G. W.

The Resurrection of Lonesome Linda

"There are horses and carriages, cows and poultry, farming implements and wagons. The building and grounds are abundantly supplied with water." — E. G. W.

that the opposition to authorizing a complete medical school was still too strong to force an issue. The Battle Creek syndrome was still viable. Hence, her answer lacked the wished-for force and direction. She had said that medical training should be started at Loma Linda and that physicians should receive their training there. She had not made clear to the satisfaction of all whether the school would graduate fully qualified physicians or merely those with the ability of physicians, but without legal qualifications.

About this time, John Burden became aware of California's revised medical practice act. His interpretation to Mrs. White was:

"It either seems like a wonderful providence, or else the enemy is seeking to entrap us to think that California, which has had the most stringent laws on medical lines, should now throw the whole thing open for any reputable school of medicine to become recognized by the State, only stipulating that its students shall pass high grades in the ten fundamental medical studies, and granting them full state recognition to practice their system of healing with perfect freedom along with other medical schools." Burden's interpretation of the law, probably inspired by wishful thinking, was erroneous, as will be noted later.

"O, how I long to see the sick and the suffering coming to this Institution.... The patients could live out of doors a large part of the time.... Rational methods for the cure of disease will be used in a variety of ways. Drugs will be discarded." — E. G. W.

183

Another council was held in Loma Linda on February 9, 1908. By this time, the majority present believed that some of the anticipated graduates of the medical-evangelistic course should be groomed to qualify for becoming fully licensed. In support of this conviction, the council recommended the enlargement of classroom and laboratory facilities. They had nothing yet comparable to a teaching hospital. It was understood that the Loma Linda council's recommendations would have to clear the General Conference Spring Council in Washington. Elders Burden and W. C. White wrote letters in an effort to influence those who would be in attendance. Mrs. White warned Burden against proposing expensive actions for which money might not be forthcoming. She stressed simplicity and the other guidelines so often mentioned by her. Despite the efforts of those hoping for action on a medical school, the reports of the council as published in the April and May *Review and Herald* indicated that the matter of Loma Linda and a medical school were not even considered.

Time moved along with no decision. A total of 112 students enrolled in 1907-08 and 120 in 1908-09, including eight in the first year of the medical-evangelistic course and seven in the second year—all no doubt medical students hoping to become licensed to practice medicine.

By this time, Burden must have perceived that his previous interpretation of California State law to Ellen White was incorrect. He decided to get reliable firsthand information. On October 3, 1908, Dr. J. Park Dougall, probably representing the California State Board of Medical Examiners, replied:

"In reference to your inquiries, would say that according to the present law a recognized medical college must conform to the requirements of the Association of American Medical Colleges, that stipulation being a part of the law. . . . The colleges to become a member of the aforesaid association must have been in existence long enough to graduate its first four-year class. This covers the point of buildings, laboratories, and equipment. The point of faculty must not be forgotten, as investigations are held frequently both interstate and intrastate. Unless your college would conform to the requirements; your diplomas would not be recognized under the present state law."

The only reason why this information was not requested much earlier in the sequence of Loma Linda events seems to have been the paralyzing effect of indecision on men having a personal sense of purpose without a clear mandate from the trustees. Although adequate documentary evidence seems to be unavailable, apparently John Burden's dual positions of chairman of the board of trustees and business manager locked in the institution's president as academic head of the institution and limited his opportunity for dynamic leadership. Probably, this situation was a factor in President Howell's decision to resign. Likewise, the problem may have influenced President Abbott to serve only two years.

Because there seemed to be a willingness at the top church level to bypass the central core of Loma Linda's problem, the Southern California Conference executive committee and the Loma Linda trustees prepared to submit resolutions to the General Conference session in June, 1909. They requested that Loma Linda be officially included in the family of Seventh-day Adventist colleges. All the resolutions from Loma Linda were reduced to one recommendation which passed after much discussion, but which because of its ambiguity meant virtually nothing to Loma Linda and was not uniformly understood:

"We recommend, that those qualifying for medical practice secure such preliminary and medical education as is accepted in this country and abroad."

This recommendation probably meant that students wishing to qualify for medical practice should secure their premedical and medical education in harmony with the laws of the country in which they hoped to practice. Such counsel was obvious and not needed. It offered no help to Loma Linda. When Burden asked Ellen White, "What shall we do now?" she replied, "Go straight ahead."

Before leaving Washington, Mrs. White delivered a pointed address to the General Conference Committee. A few days later, the committee passed several resolutions concerning Loma Linda, one of which was that the Southern California Conference authorize the Loma Linda board to apply for a charter. This was one way to say that Loma Linda was the child of the local conference and not of the General Conference. This thought was underscored by a proviso that the General Conference disclaimed any financial responsibility for the project.

When the Autumn Council of the General

Conference convened at Union College, Lincoln, Nebraska, in October of the same year, a letter came from Ellen White. She came out definitely and positively for a medical school. On the floor of the council, Elder I. H. Evans, General Conference treasurer, made a stirring appeal on behalf of Loma Linda. W. A. Ruble, medical secretary of the General Conference, strongly supported Loma Linda. The concluding resolution was brief but favorable, and passed unanimously. It directed Loma Linda to secure a charter for the college, authorizing the establishment of a school of medicine, "that it may develop as the opening providence and the instruction from the Spirit of God may indicate." John Burden was pleased and reported enthusiastically to Ellen White.

The college secured a charter from the State of California on December 9, 1909, in the name of the College of Medical Evangelists, in harmony with a name change ordered by the trustees. The college was empowered to "establish and maintain, carry on and conduct, literary, scientific, medical, dental, and pharmaceutical, and medical missionary colleges or seminaries of learning." The college was authorized to grant degrees in the liberal arts and sciences, dentistry, and medicine.

Several weeks later, at a Pacific Union Conference session held in Mountain View, California, denominational leaders again gave attention to the seemingly unsolvable problem of trying to finance and staff a genuine school of medicine. They decided to ask Sister White for a clarification. Did she mean, they queried her, a sort of Bible school where "treatment of simple diseases" would also be taught, to prepare students to do more effective missionary work? Or was it to be "a fully equipped medical school that teaches the Bible and the truth . . . but that gives such a thorough training along medical lines as will qualify the students who take the course to pass state board examinations and become registered, qualified physicians for public work"?

Ellen White replied by letter that "the medical school at Loma Linda is to be of the highest order," and she went on to spell out what she meant by that.

I. H. Evans, now a General Conference vice-president, endorsed the plan enthusiastically: "We have before us tonight a plain, straightforward statement from Sister White in regard to the establishment of a medical school. There is no guesswork about it. . . . The question is, Will we follow the counsel given?"

Other leaders, including of course John Burden, agreed. Arthur G. Daniells, General Conference president, wrote from Battle Creek that the General Conference Committee had "accepted the decisions arrived at in the Pacific Union Conference. We shall now take hold of this enterprise and do the best we can to assist in carrying it forward."

A reorganization council meeting at Loma Linda, May 6-12, 1910, resulted in the election of Wells Allen Ruble, M.D., as president and Dr. Abbott as dean. John Burden resigned as board chairman but continued as business manager. Elder G. A. Irwin was elected chairman of the board.

During this council session, and for the first time in its brief struggle for life, the College of Medical Evangelists had on its campus at one time representative groups from the General Conference, six union conferences, the Southern California Conference, and the original incorporators. The transfer of Loma Linda Sanitarium assets to the College of Medical Evangelists on June 15 made the sanitarium legally an integral part of the college. The 1910 council also defined the constituency, named a board of trustees, outlined a curriculum, and elected a faculty.

The assembled representatives at last began to perceive the importance of developing a fully accredited school of medicine.

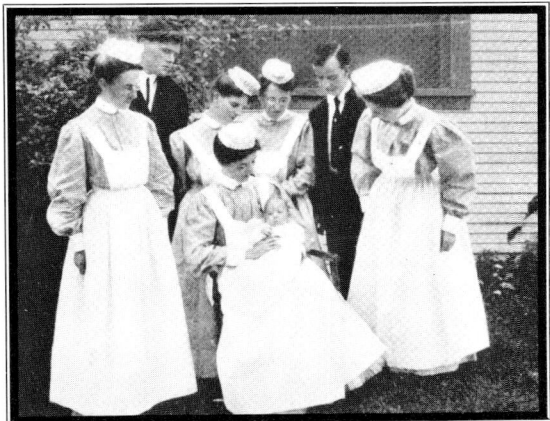

Loma Linda's first class in nursing. "We shall need to secure competent physicians and nurses, —men and women who are true and faithful; and who can be relied on; men and women who live in constant dependence upon the great Healer."—E. G. W.

The Vision Bold

"The Securing of this Property...

IS
A MIRACLE
THAT
SHOULD OPEN
THE EYES
OF OUR UNDERSTANDING.
IF
SUCH
MANIFEST WORKINGS
OF
GOD DO NOT GIVE
US A NEW
EXPERIENCE,
WHAT
WILL?"
—ELLEN WHITE.

Ellen White speaks at the dedication services of Loma Linda Sanitarium April 15, 1906, before an audience of about 500 including invited dignitaries from Riverside, Colton, San Bernardino, and Redlands. "Loma Linda is to be not only a sanitarium, but an educational center. With the possession of this place comes the weighty responsibility of making the work of the institution educational in character. A school is to be established here for the training of gospel medical missionary evangelists. Much is involved in this work, and it is very essential that a right beginning be made. The Lord has a special work to be done in this part of the field."

The Resurrection of Lonesome Linda

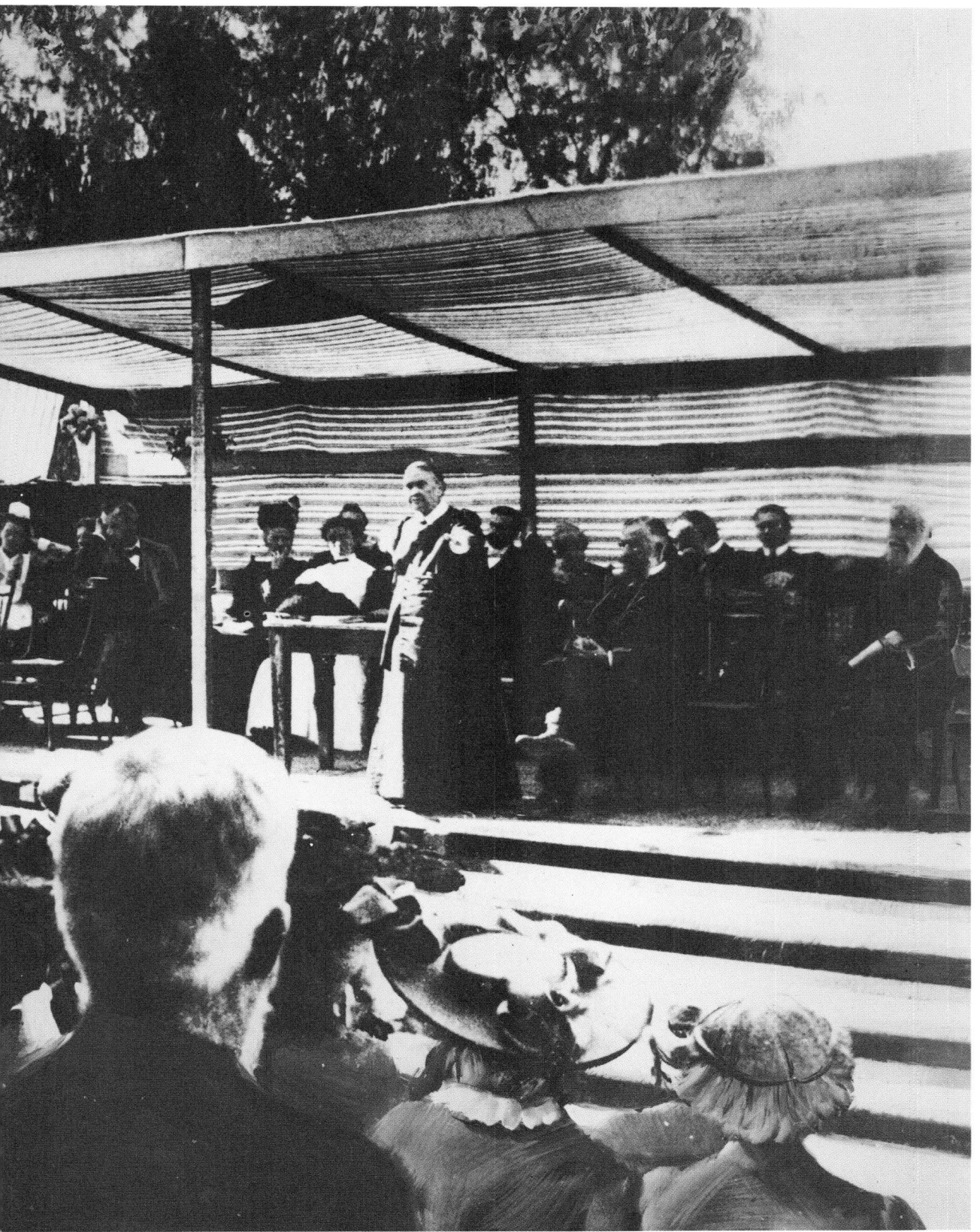

Warren E. Howell
President 1906-1907

George K. Abbott
President 1907-1909

Wells A. Ruble
President 1910-1914

Newton G. Evans
President 1914-1927

Edward H. Risley
President 1927-1928

Percy T. Magan
President 1928-1942

THEY HAVE GONE AND DONE WHAT I TOLD THEM NOT TO

THE A.M.A. NOTWITHSTANDING, THE "ONE-HORSE" SCHOOL REMAINS OPEN

In the midst of one of Dr. Percy Magan's orations—this one at the dedication of a new hospital in Los Angeles in 1918—an earth tremor shook much of southern California. The speakers' platform swayed, and the doctor ad libbed: "It takes a good-sized man to make a speech that will start an earthquake!"

Yes, and it took some good-sized men, guided constantly by an overruling Providence, to keep C.M.E. functioning in those early years—a task roughly as awesome as starting an earthquake. The job often seemed to involve turning nature out of its course. Yet, as that Providence so arranged it, men to match the mountains appeared when they had to appear.

In May, 1910, C.M.E.'s President Wells Ruble reported that things were looking up. First and second-year classes in medicine would begin on September 29, with advanced courses to be offered the following year. Eight more physicians had been recruited for the faculty, though this was not an easy task, as the college was not making the most attractive salary offers. In a letter to Dr. E. H. Risley, Ruble wrote: "I might say that physicians are accepting a salary of $20 a week. This is the most that is paid to anyone."

By the end of December, a much-needed women's residence hall neared completion. Because promised funds from various conferences came in with frustrating slowness, a planned laboratory building could not be started until the spring of 1911 or finished until after school opened in the fall.

The first instruction in anatomy took place in temporary quarters on the second floor of a bakery building in nearby Colton. When preserving fluids leaked through into the first floor, the baker protested. College management corrected the evil, and instruction continued.

Later, the City of Colton protested obnoxious odors emanating from the incinerator. The College cooperated by moving the laboratory to acceptable quarters nearer the campus but not near enough to be offensive to sanitarium patients, some of whom still had a ghoulish concept of dissection.

Seeking to strengthen the spiritual purpose of the college, President Ruble voiced his concern that the intensive work demanded by the medical curriculum would rob students of time for spiritual things. This was one reason for planning a five-year medical curriculum when the first class entered, in 1909. Ruble was reminded of the original reform features of "our medical work" by such medical missionary zealots as Dr. David Paulson, who later wrote that "as a spiritual force and as a reformatory force in the world, if we fall down on that it would be better if we had never been born."

The five-year course was also needed because students at first were admitted with only a high-school diploma. During the first year they would study preprofessional courses in the sciences. The very next year, the school upgraded its requirements for admission. It accepted a baccalaureate degree or, in lieu of it, a high school diploma plus a transcript certifying certain premedical subjects. An applicant could also enter by earning a California State Board of Medical Examiners certificate declaring that he had passed specific premedical subjects. Annual tuition was $100; matriculation was $5, paid only on entering the freshman year.

Throughout 1912, the dearth of funds for operating and building caused distress among faculty and administration. The General Conference and several union and local conferences had promised subsidies, but they were late or defaulting. When President Ruble appealed to the General Conference, Elder Daniells replied that they wished to assist by every means at their disposal, but he enclosed no check. Further, Daniells explained the plight of the eastern conferences, but he gave permission to solicit funds throughout the field.

Because hospital patients would soon be needed for clinical instruction, the board made plans to begin construction on a small hospital by September 1. They had only $4,000, and postponed the construction. Doctor Ruble was, nevertheless, able to sound an encouraging note to W. C. White when school started. A good number of new students enrolled in several classes, and only one student of the year 1911-12 failed to return. The trustees determined to construct a hospital, and the students believed that the trustees would make good their promise.

Doctor Ruble spent most of the summer of 1912 in postgraduate study at Harvard University. If he had not known previously, certainly while at Harvard he must have heard about the national scandal related to medical education in the United States. Abraham Flexner's *Medical Education in the United States and Canada*, published in 1910, exposed the deplorable state of medical education in the majority of medical schools, many of them little more than diploma mills.

The American Medical Association, when it organized in 1847, declared in its constitution these purposes: "cultivating and advancing medical knowledge; elevating the standard of medical education; promoting the usefulness, honor, and interest of the medical professional; enlightening and directing public opinion in regard to the duties, responsibilities and requirements of medical men."

The low state of medical education in the mid-nineteenth century had driven conscientious members of the profession to organize and make the above declaration. In harmony with Jacksonian laissez-faire democracy of the time, most of the states from 1830-1850 had wiped from their statute books acts regulating the practice of medicine and law. Each medical school was autonomous, and many were proprietary. The good intentions of the callow A.M.A. were useless because it had no authority but persuasion. The profession in each state had to educate its own legislature to recognize and correct the evil. This proved to be a long process. Ultimately, states organized medical boards and gave them power to examine all candidates and to license those successful in meeting the boards' standards.

The Association of American Medical Colleges, organized in 1890, recommended high school graduation as a minimum prerequisite for medicine. Soon afterward, in 1893, the Johns Hopkins University made a bachelor's degree a requirement for admission to the medical school. Many medical educators were moved by this example.

The A.M.A. reorganized in 1901, adopting state and local societies as constituent parts of the national body. The obvious need for an inquiry into medical school standards led to the establishment of the Council on Medical Education in 1904.

By 1908, the council had gathered sufficient information and had run into enough opposition from the poorer schools to justify asking an independent agency, the Carnegie Foundation for the Advancement of Teaching, to make a survey of medical education. The invitation was accepted. Mr. Abraham Flexner, an educator and scholar in the humanities, was commissioned to make the study. Accompanied by Dr. Nathan P. Colwell, secretary of the council, Flexner visited all schools in the United States and Canada.

Fred Herzer, Owen Parrett, Mr. Sutton, and Thomas Joseph plaster the old laboratory buildings in 1911.

The published report shocked the public. People began to realize that medical education in this country lagged far behind that in Europe. Mr. Flexner had visited 155 medical schools, more than all the medical schools in the rest of the world. Some had been started without approval or permission. Many students entered them without a high school diploma. Only the best schools had a four-year curriculum of six months each year.

The purifying influence of professional disapproval and public exposure was remarkable. The Council and the Association of Medical Colleges had begun a systematic classification of schools before Flexner's study, classifying all schools as A, B, or C. State boards began excluding students from examinations who had not graduated from a classified school. Most states admitted to examination only graduates of A and B schools. A diploma from a C-grade school was nearly worthless.

By the time of Flexner's report, reforms had reduced the number of four-year medical schools by more than one-half. Many of the weaker schools closed; some gained strength through university affiliation or consolidation; and some limited their curriculum to two years of basic science. Nearly all surviving were able to secure state support or endowment.

The College of Medical Evangelists launched its frail bark into the turbid stream of American medical education at the time of the greatest thrust of this reform. In some respects, there was nothing strange about Loma Linda—just another group of interested persons with little or no money deciding to start a medical school. Not a few so-called schools had been financially self-sustaining, and medical educators scarcely employed the word "budget." Only 38 of the 155 schools Flexner visited had budgets; and of these budgets only five ran into six figures. Medical education was not big business; it was still in the trade-school bracket.

President Ruble kept in touch with the changing scene. He knew that the medical school's current and foreseeable needs would make increasing financial demands on the constituency. A heavy freeze in the winter of 1913 badly damaged the citrus crop and other fruits. The financial structure in southern California was shaken to the point that holders of some of the College's notes payable demanded payment. Much of the president's correspondence in 1913 and the first half of 1914 reflected the intense financial strain under which the college administration worked.

A small hospital was completed during 1913, but it failed to attract sufficient patronage to fulfill the need for teaching beds. Another facility for attracting clinical cases was provided at 941 East First Street in Los Angeles, where a charity clinic was opened in an old store building. Called a dispensary, it was staffed principally by volunteer physicians, and proved highly successful.

Loma Linda graduating nurses, 1912

The Los Angeles County Hospital also permitted a limited amount of clinic and bedside observation.

The Loma Linda Sanitarium had patients, but it was not customary to submit private patients to teaching routine at that time. Further, the patients were usually unwilling. The San Bernardino County Hospital's affiliation with the school was still not mature enough to offer a solution to the problem.

The best prospect for clinical teaching facilities in the spring of 1914 seemed to be in Los Angeles. The First Street dispensary and the Los Angeles County Hospital saved the first senior class from a dearth of patient contact. Writing optimistically in April 1914 to Dr. George Thomason, President Ruble declared: "I feel that the school is on the strongest basis that it has been, and that we shall make good in every line." After noting various improvements, he concluded with this thought: "We shall not be a whit behind any school in advantages offered from this time on." Subsequent events did not quite justify this burst of optimism.

Six senior students graduated in June, 1914. The school as yet had had no classification, but it had a state charter; therefore, the graduates were admitted to the state board examination. The failure of two brought some gloom, but President Ruble attributed the misfortune to some faltering in getting the curriculum into operation, and to years of uncertainty regarding the status of the school.

Perhaps Dr. Ruble's deeper inner feelings were revealed when in August he resigned his duties as president. His successor was to be Newton Evans, M.D., a Cornell graduate (1900) who had taught pathology and histology at the American Medical Missionary College, practiced medicine in Kentucky for nine years, and taught pathology part-time at the University of Tennessee. He had also served as medical director, assisted by Dr. Lillian Magan, of the Madison Sanitarium near Nashville for a time.

When Dr. Ruble became president in 1910, he had expressed to Dr. Evans his disappointment that Evans was not selected for the post. The board agreed that Evans was qualified in many respects, but felt that he lacked experience in Seventh-day Adventist educational work. They considered the American Medical Missionary

Loma Linda nurses, Mrs. Wellesley Magan and Mrs. Celian Andross

192

College, during the years of Evans's faculty membership, as something less than representative of the church. Similarly, Madison Sanitarium was under a sort of sub rosa disapproval because of some of the independent policies of the founders, Edward A. Sutherland and Percy T. Magan.

Medical education authorities now required a thorough inspection of new medical schools. Secretary Nathan P. Colwell of the Council on Medical Education had made an informal visit in 1912 with no intention of classifying the school. He was friendly and polite, but recommended that the promoters of the College of Medical Evangelists abandon their attempt to establish an approved medical school. He admitted that the medical profession was out to crush "one-horse medical schools."

Some months later, back in his Chicago office, Dr. Colwell scribbled a memo in pencil that a man named Salisbury (probably Wilbur D. Salisbury, business manager of Loma Linda Sanitarium in 1913), had called at Colwell's office and reported that the College was going ahead with plans for an approved school. After the interview, Colwell added the laconic note, "They have gone and done what I told them not to."

President Evans had assumed his duties in Loma Linda only a few weeks before Dr. Colwell arrived in December for his first official inspection. Colwell no doubt complimented the administration on its two-year premedical requirement and other progressive aspects. But he could hardly have endorsed the scattered, disorganized provisions for clinical instruction. The Council on Medical Education, meeting in February, 1915, gave the school a "C" rating. This was in spite of a 1911 board action which had raised the debt ceiling, already shockingly high, to $400,000 to help upgrade the school above the "C" level.

In his critique of C.M.E., Dr. Colwell observed, among other things, that "it was claimed that there are ten full-time teachers, and that the total expense for salaries amounts to $15,368. This sum, however, includes expenses for janitor service and other help about the institution. One of the full-time teachers receives $1,200 per year; four receive a salary of $1,100 each, and one receives $1,000."

Despite their hopefulness, President Evans and others could not have been surprised at the low rating. By this time medical educators understood certain requirements: First, a premedical education must precede admission to medical school, a standard already announced at Loma Linda. Second, medical sciences such as anatomy and physiology must be taught by experienced teachers trained in their respective areas rather than by practicing physicians giving part time. Third, medicine must be learned not just from books and lectures, but chiefly from observation of the sick; hospitals and clinics are as necessary as laboratories; and a school should never be constrained to make casual faculty appointments merely to gain access to certain hospital wards. Fourth, to secure public support and maintain high academic standards, medical schools should be affiliated with universities. The College of Medical Evangelists was noticeably substandard in the second and third areas, and could foresee no way to achieve the goal of the fourth.

The Council of Medical Education concluded that any school conducted in harmony with these precepts would cost much more than the amount received in students' fees. The solution would be to develop generous support from some other source.

This was precisely the problem at Loma Linda. From the first, no one seemed to object to Adventist youth planning careers in the health field, preferably in an Adventist institution. However, years passed before it became reasonably certain that the institution would offer a four-year course in medicine qualifying graduates for state board examinations. Obviously, student fees and scant sanitarium earnings could not pay costs, yet no unit of the church organization volunteered to assume financial responsibility. Overextended as they were, local and union conferences and the General Conference had practical reasons for deferring responsibility.

In 1913, the General Conference showed signs of recognizing its duty to give leadership in clarifying the issue. In its quadrennial session in May and June, the conference endorsed Loma Linda as a center for training physicians. It was proposed that the North American Division advance the sum of $17,550 for completion of the Loma Linda Hospital and the alteration and furnishing of the First Street Clinic. They referred the resolution to the finance committee of the division and the General Conference for a joint solution. Whatever arrangements were worked out, Loma Linda management found it encouraging to see the responsibility accepted at a high level.

When Newton Evans became president, rumors that the school might yet be cut back to a two-year curriculum occasionally circulated. Faint hearts in scattered administrative posts still feared the prospect of having to raise substantial funds in spite of all the positive resolutions, enabling acts, and monies promised. The whole subject again came before the General Conference Autumn Council when it met at Loma Linda in November, 1915, in conjunction with the constituency.

Many delegates opposed continuing a four-year school. It was a tense and troublesome time. Friends and brothers took opposing views. On the evening of November 10, a group of warm defenders of the four-year school invited Elder Daniells to meet with them. They continued throughout much of the night, earnestly reviewing the ten-year history of the project and Ellen White's instruction.

Daniells was convinced. Standing before the council the next day, he admitted having had fears and doubts concerning Loma Linda. But he now declared his faith and conviction that they should go forward. His endorsement was powerful and persuasive.

After unrestricted discussion, the council advised the board to carry out the full four-year medical course as recommended by Ellen White and others. They also approved the construction of a $60,000 hospital in Los Angeles. Elder Daniells then clinched the action with well-chosen words:

"We must square up to this now. We have considered this matter seriously and prayerfully, and have finally reached the decision set before you in these recommendations. Is there anything else in this world to do but to encourage our young people who contemplate taking the medical course, to go to this school? When we pass this recommendation, we commit ourselves to the earnest support of this school. . . . We do not say, Stop. We say, go on and maintain this school and make it a success. When I vote for that, I feel in duty bound from this day on to do all I can by my counsel and influence to help them carry the school through successfully, and that I am pledged to do."

This session on November 11, 1915, was the psychological turning point in the history of C.M.E. President Evans had a clear mandate, unencumbered with crippling reservations. Major problems remained to be solved, but he could now work with the competence and vigor for which he was known.

Knowing when he came to Loma Linda the

Newton Evans, M.D., physician, scientist, leader, man of great stature in the development of College of Medical Evangelists.

need for a clinical division in Los Angeles, President Evans asked the board to name Percy T. Magan, M.D., dean of the school with specific instruction to plan and develop the Los Angeles campus. Dr. Magan attended the November meeting. He suspected a certain low cunning on the part of the opposition and reported it to Dr. David Paulson in his own peculiar way:

"We have just passed through one of the biggest battles in the history of the denomination, nominally over Loma Linda, but in reality involving the integrity of the spirit of prophecy [the counsel of Ellen White] and our belief in the same.

"A delegation of preachers, at least those whom Elder Haskell would style 'The Magnates' were determined to kill the school. I do not mean that they would admit this in so many words, but they were determined to fix it either by killing it outright or else putting it in a place where it was impossible for it to exist."

Writing to Elder Daniells, Magan complimented him on his "firm straight attitude" and noted that the forensic struggle was "the first big test which had come up after the death of the prophet," meaning Ellen White, who had died on July 16 of the same year at the age of eighty-seven. Now those who had frequently called on her for help in decision making would need to

Dr. Alfred Shryock in his office on second floor of the old North Laboratory. He joined C.M.E. in 1910, and at the time of his death in 1950 he was the only faculty member who had taught every class admitted to the school of medicine.

study her published counsels and apply the undergirding principles. Looking back on the early struggle at Loma Linda, Arthur L. White, secretary of the Ellen G. White Publications, explained:

"The spirit of prophecy counsels were never given to take the place of initiative, study, faith, or hard work. Rather, the Lord through His servant set before us guiding principles and sounded needed cautions—all of which served to guide and guard the church in its many activities."

Both Evans and Magan subscribed to this principle and acted accordingly. They did not always agree, but each had some capacity to bend when necessary.

Born in Ireland in 1867, Magan had come to America as a willful lad of sixteen. His father had bound him to a Red Cloud, Nebraska, Irish farmer, who promised to make him a great cattle rancher. The disillusioned lad managed to have the pact with the farmer broken. His father disowned him; the young man was on his own.

He came under the influence of two Seventh-day Adventist evangelists, joined the church, and went to Battle Creek College. Ellen White early recognized in this energetic young man a teacher and administrator of great talent. Within a few years, he was an ordained minister teaching history and religion in Battle Creek College. Later, as dean, he and President Sutherland decided the college should be moved to Berrien Springs, Michigan, where they founded Emmanuel Missionary College. After this institution was well established, the two men moved on to Madison, Tennessee, where they founded the Madison Sanitarium. Then both took the M.D. degree at the University of Tennessee in 1914. Being both a clergyman and a physician, Magan could fraternize with men of both professions. He knew how to relate himself to the sensitive feelings between the two. This he usually did admirably, but at times to the discomfort of the clergy. Some critics felt that he made far too frequent use of his Irish sense of humor.

For example, speaking of the peccadillos of young people, he remarked, "You know, when the good Lord had all the holy angels with Him in heaven, right under His thumb, one-third of them went wrong! Now folks expect us [the faculty] to do better than that right here!"

Officially scolded for his unauthorized purchase of half a block of land in Boyle Heights, Los Angeles, Magan was then asked, "What will you do with all this land?"

Percy replied, "I plan to put up a building and manufacture yellow pups!"

With the First Street Clinic already in good operation by 1914, the possibility of building a hospital in Los Angeles was frequently discussed. As early as 1911, Ellen White had presented

Left: Abraham Flexner exposed the deplorable state of medical education in America in his report published in 1910. As a result, numerous medical diploma mills were put out of business. Right: Dr. Nathan P. Colwell fully intended to close C.M.E., and when he learned that the school intended to remain open, he observed, "They have gone and done what I told them not to." Later, he became an unstinting admirer of the Adventist institution, describing his work with the A.M.A. as "a little bit of a job, while you are doing the really big things of the world."

"the necessity of broadening our plans to include the cities in the San Bernardino Valley and Los Angeles." When asked if it would be "right to give the last two years of instruction in Los Angeles or if we should hold all the work at Loma Linda," she advised, as recorded by W. C. White, "that we do in Loma Linda just as much of the work as could be done acceptably there, and carry the remainder to Los Angeles."

On May 9, 1915, during her final illness, her son reported to her that a church member in the East had offered to make a liberal gift to the college for a students' home and a hospital in Los Angeles. Deeply moved, Mrs. White replied, "I am glad you told me this," and concluded, "I have been in perplexity about Loma Linda, and this has given me courage and joy."

Elder White's report of his mother's hearty endorsement of plans for a hospital in Los Angeles, which came to bear her name, strengthened the hands of college trustees and officers and gave impetus to the campaign for funds.

The United States declared war on the German Empire on April 6, 1917. Soon thereafter the Adventist Church restated its historic position of noncombatancy, but affirmed its loyalty to the Constitution and the Federal Government. Some officials were nettled by the noncombatant stand, but the college's offer to organize a general hospital staff for the army cooled the critics.

At first, a plan evolved whereby second, third, and fourth-year students, interns, and younger faculty members who enlisted in the Medical Reserve Corps before receiving a draft call would be deferred if they attended a well-recognized medical school. However, a "C" rating did not constitute recognition, and C.M.E. students began receiving induction orders.

Evans and Magan went into action. They recruited a friend, George Hare, M.D., of Fresno, and headed for Chicago. Hare, a booster of the college, was president of the American Academy of Medicine, a blue-blood professional society. A conference with George H. Simmons, secretary of the A.M.A., and N. P. Colwell, secretary of the Council on Medical Education, pointed the way. Upgrading was the only solution, and even this might come too late.

Colwell offered to inspect the school at an early date. Magan was sent to the surgeon general of the Army in Washington. He asked whether, if N. P. Colwell inspected C.M.E. very soon and gave it a "B" classification, their students would be deferred and their draftees returned to school. The answer was favorable.

To prepare for the inspection, Magan dispatched letters to key personnel at Loma Linda and Los Angeles, where the White Memorial Hospital was under construction. To Alfred Q. Shryock, M.D., whose duties covered a wide front, he wrote:

"Now please do your best to have everything in Loma Linda in apple pie order so that nothing will go awry when he [Dr. Colwell] comes. The hospital records should all be put in as good condition as time will permit."

He ordered the hospital construction superintendent in Los Angeles to "spare no pains to push the work on the surgery building as fast as you can and a good deal faster. Get more men, get students to help, but get that building as nearly completed as you can. . . . Get that filthy crop of tin cans, rubber boots, cast-off clothing, and other elements of the abomination of desolation reaped with the sickle of the reaper and burned in your incinerator."

Dr. Colwell inspected the school thoroughly

In 1915 Arthur G. Daniells, president of the General Conference of Seventh-day Adventists, pledged support of the entire denomination to C.M.E. "We must square up to this now. . . . We do not say, Stop. We say, Go on and maintain this school and make it a success. When I vote for that, I feel in duty bound . . . to help carry the school through successfully, and that I am pledged to do."

on November 7, 1917. Being sure of the Council's ultimate decision, he notified the surgeon general of the "B" classification. Magan informed the draftees of the favorable prospects. All were back at Loma Linda, except one, by January 1.

However, the government ordered deferred students to enlist in the Student Army Training Corps on the campus of their mother university. The school had too few students to form a training unit, so arrangements were made for Loma Linda students to drill with Redlands University students, and Los Angeles students with Occidental College students. Then the church refused to authorize students to participate in any SATC units, fearing it would compromise the Adventist noncombatant position.

President Evans hurried to Washington to find some solution to the problem, but found none. While gloom settled over both campuses, draft boards began mailing calls to duty. Five were notified. Then came November 11, 1918. The five draftees were turned back as they boarded the train for boot camp. Prayers of thanksgiving ascended.

During the war years, Dr. Magan continued his fund-raising for the hospital. Many rebuffed him—those who had not yet caught the gleam that marked the 1915 council in Loma Linda. In his usual pungent style, the Irishman wrote: "I am being fought on this medical school proposition from one end of the country to the other. . . . Opposition of every name and nature that the devil can manufacture, invent, or imagine, has been brought to bear against the whole thing; but God lives and reigns, and in spite of all this I have gathered a pledge list of over $40,000 positive pledges, and the people who pledged to me are sticking loyally."

After one of his many struggles with boards and finances, Magan wrote to his friend Sutherland: "But the Lord has helped me to bat some of these fellows over the head, and things are looking up."

A group of women headed by Mrs. S. N. Haskell helped Magan with the fund raising. A potential donor who had promised a sizable sum to the Madison, Tennessee, institution became interested in the Los Angeles project, and with the blessing of Sutherland and his colleagues, the donor gave the money to Magan's project, partly to help dismay Magan's critics who had predicted he would fail to raise $60,000.

In the spring of 1916, Magan and a few others were convinced that purchase of the south half of the 300 block of North Boyle Avenue, authorized by the board for the hospital site, would not suffice. One day Magan told Evans he would not show his Irish face again until he had the cash for purchase of the northern half of the block. At the next board meeting, the dean reported his success due to the generosity of several friends.

The hospital building had advanced far enough early in 1918 to set April 21 as a day for dedication. At the appointed hour, a crowd of over 2,000 had gathered to hear Magan's far-famed rhetoric. It was at this time that the earthquake struck, prompting Magan to say, "It takes a good-sized man to make a speech that will start an earthquake!" The crowd soon quieted down.

With the war problems out of the way, the college stepped up its efforts to qualify for a class "A" rating. The size of classes increased rapidly as medicine gained popularity as a career among Adventist youth. When the freshman class

Loma Linda Sanitarium's first motor transportation.

of 1919 reached fifty in number, some trustees clamored for a 50 percent cut to ward off overproduction. Others feared that medicine would attract the better students from the various Adventist colleges, leaving the second-rate minds to pursue the ministry. Ultimately, there were sufficient qualified candidates for both professions.

In 1920, C.M.E. found itself in a position to be a Good Samaritan. The University of Southern California School of Medicine closed its doors, leaving its senior class with no school in which to complete its last year. Transfers from one school to another conventionally took place between the second and third years. With the guidance of the Council on Medical Education, the two institutions devised an agreeable plan by which U.S.C. seniors finished on the C.M.E. Los Angeles campus, but received their degrees from U.S.C. When C.M.E. had received its charter in 1909, five other medical schools operated in Los Angeles. The U.S.C. School of Medicine was the last of the five to close, leaving C.M.E. for a few years the lone such institution in southern California.

The next inspection was set for May 15, 1921. W. E. Musgrave, M.D., headed the visiting committee. In their report, they explained why they could not yet recommend the "A" rating to the Council on Medical Education. First, the top administrative structure should be changed so that the president would be above the business manager, who at the time was also the chief executive officer of the board. While it seemed necessary to continue operating the two campuses, the headquarters of the medical school should be in Los Angeles. The library was deficient and should be built up. The teaching staff needed still more strengthening. An adequate budget should be provided. There should be an executive committee of the board to coordinate the administration and see that board policies were carried out.

The trustees resented the report; some even insinuated that Dr. Magan wrote it. Even though Magan had the facility for planting suggestions, the organizational changes called for were elementary for good administrative practice. Months later, in the spring of 1922, the board voted to reorganize the school as recommended by the committee. The A.M.A. was pleased with C.M.E.'s progress, and in November of that year Dr. Colwell attended a banquet at the Los Angeles campus. In his speech, as quoted by Magan, Colwell said:

"When the Seventh-day Adventists first started . . . a number of us felt that they were doomed for defeat. I told them over and over again not to make a start. But today I must confess that their faith has triumphed over my unbelief. Some years ago Dr. Magan took me over the place which their hospital plant now covers. It was then a mass of weeds, cockleburs, and there were two or three sorry-looking animals feeding upon it. Dr. Magan remarked to me that someday we would have a great medical institution there. I thought to myself: You poor soul, you do not know what you are talking about; you will never be able to have a first-class medical school; but today I walk over that same block covered with beautiful buildings, and veritable hive of medical activities. . . . I am almost certain as to the kind of report I will make, and I am sure you will all be satisfied with it."

Colwell then wrote Magan officially: "After watching the efforts you have been making to develop your medical school during the past several years, it is my most pleasing duty to inform you that at its business meeting on November 14, the Council of Medical Education and Hospitals voted that the College of Medical Evangelists be granted a Class A rating."

Colwell later told Magan, "I feel ashamed of myself sitting here rating you people, which is a little bit of a job, while you are doing the really big things of the world. You have done wonders in your school, and I am proud of you; and while you have not converted me to the seventh-day Sabbath as yet, you have converted me on practically everything else about your medical work."

Dr. Magan remarked, "Thus endeth that chapter which has been a long and dreary one."

"They Have Gone and Done What I Told Them Not To"

Above left: Student nurses picnic in Santa Ana Canyon, 1912. Above right: Group of students in San Bernardino Mountains. Left: Student nurses and friends cavort on Kate Lindsay lawn, 1914.

In 1927, Dr. Evans wished to be relieved of presidential duties. Dr. Edward H. Risley, professor of biochemistry, succeeded him. But Risley, not captivated by the job, wished to be relieved after one year. Dean Magan, eminently qualified and willing, assumed the presidency in 1928. Doctor Risley became dean of the Loma Linda Division and Dr. Evans accepted the position of chief pathologist and director of laboratories of the Los Angeles County Hospital. In order to make the most of Dr. Evans's talents, the board elected him vice-president of C.M.E., which post he accepted on a voluntary basis. As the representative of C.M.E. on the Medical Advisory Board of the County Hospital, Dr. Magan, with Dr. Evans in the County Hospital assignment, accomplished much in elevating the standing of the County Hospital as a teaching institution.

How did the College of Medical Evangelists succeed in rising, phoenixlike, from the ruins of Battle Creek's A.M.M.C. while occupying the site of twice-defunct "Lonesome Linda"?

Dr. Magan has provided the best possible answer: "If we had listened to the counsel of worldlings, I do not suppose we ever would have started our schools, our sanitariums, our publishing houses...all of which have grown out of very feeble and very imperfect beginnings, started, however, in the fear and under the hand of a mighty God, according to the word of His servant, the prophet."

Later he reminisced on a time of adversity for the school: "There is something about the experience of having the burden of a great crisis rolled upon you when you are alone which drives you very close to God. I was on my way to save the only medical school in all the world which bore the name of God....

"I remembered the prayers which so often fell from the lips of Ellen G. White, of John Burden, of many another soul who struggled to launch the school. I, too, had prayed, and it came into my mind that prayers do not die when they leave our lips; they are 'nigh unto the Lord our God day and night.' I knew that the prayers offered long ago were still doing duty before the great white throne, and I was comforted."

The aging little lady from Elmshaven had predicted, "A school will be established here.... Battle Creek is going down. God will reestablish His medical work at this place."

This prophecy met ample fulfillment in the closing of American Medical Missionary College, and in the demise of Dr. John Kellogg's grand-hotel colossus, to which the great of earth had made their pilgrimages. Battle Creek as a Mecca for health seekers greatly diminished. (However, Battle Creek Sanitarium has survived, and again operates under Adventist ownership.)

The practical message of good health, closely linked with spiritual truths—the philosophy that created the Western Health Reform Institute in 1866—has flowered in hundreds of places around the planet.

As the Adventist medical stronghold shifted westward, Battle Creek influenced and strengthened it in various ways. Battle Creek graduates took their places as leaders and staff members at Loma Linda and other health institutions. Will K. Kellogg, who had cooked and rolled wheat and corn in the Battle Creek Sanitarium kitchen, always referred to Adventists as "our people," and gave substantial gifts to Loma Linda Sanitarium and White Memorial Hospital.

The spirit of philanthropy so notable in the careers of the Kellogg brothers still pervades hospitals, clinics, even river launches and airplanes, in some sixty countries. In many areas of the world, modern counterparts of John Burden still venture forward with shining faith, wrestling with impossibly small budgets to accomplish extraordinary results. There are still godly physicians and other practitioners of the healing arts who, in the tradition of David and Mary Paulson, minister to the unfortunate with little thought for themselves.

On the occasion of Dr. John Kellogg's last birthday, in 1943, the Battle Creek *Enquirer-*

A C.M.E. medical intern and nurse make an outside OB call in Los Angeles in the 1920's.

Patients at Boyle Avenue dispensary.

Loma Linda's spiritual center for three decades. In 1909, John Burden called a meeting of workers to consider building a church. Fred Drake designed and built the new sanctuary, which stood until 1938, when the Hill Church replaced it.

News headlined: "His Work Felt by the Whole World—Dr. John Harvey Kellogg a Factor in Civilization." This was not an overstatement. However, the short little physician dressed in white was only a part—a prominent part, to be sure—of a health-reform movement and philosophy which has increasingly proved its scientific truthfulness and humanitarian worth on a global scale.

Horace B. Powell, biographer of W. K. Kellogg, has written: "It would be difficult to overemphasize the tremendous force upon the history of this nation exerted by several denominational churches. . . . The Seventh-day Adventists with their tenets of the simple restorative methods of nature, and the use of hydrotherapy and vegetarianism, have made an indelible mark upon our country."

The godly example and wise counsels of the remarkable little woman of Elmshaven, together with the ingenuity, devotion, and faith of the other pioneers—these remain as a priceless legacy to the church and the world. Undoubtedly, their bequest benefits many more of earth's inhabitants today with spiritual and physcial health and healing than when the pioneers still lived.

"THE LORD IS WELL PLEASED WITH WHAT YOU HAVE ALREADY DONE HERE AT LOMA LINDA. . . . I AM SURPRISED, HAPPILY SURPRISED, TO SEE EVERYTHING LOOKING SO WELL. IT IS BEYOND MY EXPECTATIONS. AND NOW LET EVERYONE STRIVE TO KEEP IT SO, AND LABOR FOR IMPROVEMENT."
—ELLEN WHITE.

Three aging warriors who strove mightily to make Loma Linda a medical center of the highest order: Drs. George W. Thomason, Percy T. Magan, and Newton G. Evans.

POSTSCRIPT

The story does not end here, but continues onward in both time and space. That which started so inauspiciously in Michigan in the 1860's has grown into a worldwide ministry of health and healing. Regrettably, it is not possible within this book's scope to chronicle the entire story of ever-enlarging Seventh-day Adventist efforts, personal and institutional, "to make man whole." Therefore, the sanitariums in Stoneham, Massachusetts; Washington, D.C.; Portland, Oregon; Orlando, Florida; Willowdale, Ontario; Kettering, Ohio; Boulder and Denver, Colorado; and many others, each with its story to tell, have not been included here. With the single exception of Australia, fascinating chapters on the growth in lands other than North America also remain untold. The health food business, which first sprouted in the sanitariums, is dealt with only in its earlier stages in America and Australia. Much more might be told if space permitted.

The following list names some of the larger medical institutions (with the number of patient beds) which have not otherwise been featured in this book. The list must be viewed as representative; it is by no means complete.

In the United States and Canada

Ardmore Seventh-day Adventist Hospital, Ardmore, Oklahoma, 105
Boulder Memorial Hospital, Boulder, Colorado, 115
Castle Memorial Hospital, Kailua, Hawaii, 101
Feather River Hospital, Paradise, California, 94
Florida Hospital, Orlando, Florida, 569
Hackettstown Community Hospital, Hackettstown, New Jersey, 106
Kettering Medical Center, Kettering, Ohio, 407
Madison Hospital, Madison, Tennessee, 215
New England Memorial Hospital, Stoneham, Massachusetts, 291
North York Branson Hospital, Willowdale, Ontario, Canada, 447
Porter Memorial Hospital, Denver, Colorado, 290
Portland Adventist Hospital, Portland, Oregon, 287
Riverside Hospital, Nashville, Tennessee, 50
Shawnee Mission Medical Center, Shawnee Mission, Kansas, 198
Simi Valley Adventist Hospital, Simi Valley, California, 198
Tempe Community Hospital, Tempe, Arizona, 81
Walker Memorial Hospital, Avon Park, Florida, 99
Washington Adventist Hospital, Takoma Park, Maryland, 315
White Memorial Medical Center, Los Angeles, California, 302

In Other Countries

Bandung Adventist Hospital, Bandung, Indonesia, 150
Bangkok Adventist Hospital, Bangkok, Thailand, 180
Belém Adventist Hospital, Belém, Brazil, 100
Bella Vista Hospital, Mayaguez, Puerto Rico, 82
Berlin Hospital, Berlin, Germany, 346
Giffard Memorial Hospital, Nuzvid, India, 131
Hong Kong Adventist Hospital, Hong Kong, 108
Hultafors Sanitarium, Bollebygd, Sweden, 155
Kanye Hospital, Botswana, Africa, 200
Karachi Hospital, Karachi, Pakistan, 120
Lake Geneva Sanitarium, Gland, Switzerland, 100
Malamulo Hospital and Leprosarium, Malawi, Africa, 109

Maluti Hospital, Ficksburg, South Africa, 175
Manila Sanitarium and Hospital, Manila, Philippines, 151
Montemorelos Sanitarium and Hospital, Montemorelos, Mexico, 50
Port-of-Spain Adventist Hospital, Trinidad, W. I., 70
River Plate Sanitarium and Hospital, Puiggari, Argentina, 171
Silvestre Adventist Hospital, Rio de Janeiro, Brazil, 120
Skodsborg Sanitarium, Skodsborg, Denmark, 270
Skogli Sanitarium, Lillehammer, Norway, 120
Taiwan Adventist Hospital, Taipei, Taiwan, 138
Tokyo Sanitarium and Hospital, Tokyo, Japan, 120

Acknowledgments

Administrative officers and public relations personnel of the Kellogg Company, the Kellogg Foundation, Battle Creek Sanitarium Hospital, Review and Herald Publishing Association, Pacific Press Publishing Association, Saint Helena Hospital and Health Center, Glendale Adventist Hospital, Paradise Valley Hospital, Loma Linda University, Andrews University, and Hinsdale Sanitarium and Hospital have been most helpful in making available information, photographs, and memorabilia to illustrate this book. Dr. Thomas S. Whitelock shared valuable family pictures.

Arthur L. White reviewed the manuscript and made helpful corrections and suggestions. Kenneth W. Wilson copy edited the manuscript, and Arbie Kreye typed it.

In addition to original sources consulted, published books and periodicals which provided data on early Adventist medical history include: *The Story of Our Health Message*, by D. E. Robinson (Southern Publishing Association, 1943); *His Name Was David*, by Caroline L. Clough (Review and Herald, 1955); *The Original Has This Signature—W. K. Kellogg*, by Horace B. Powell (Prentice-Hall, 1956); *John Harvey Kellogg, M.D.*, by Richard W. Schwarz (Southern Publishing Association, 1970); *For God and C. M. E.*, by Merlin L. Neff (Pacific Press, 1964); *The Advent Message in the Golden West*, by Harold O. McCumber (Pacific Press, 1946, 1968); *Seventh-day Adventist Encyclopedia* (Review and Herald, 1966); and *Advent Review and Sabbath Herald*, various issues.

BIOGRAPHICAL SKETCHES

GODFREY T. ANDERSON (*Introduction*) received the M.S. degree at Northwestern University and the Ph.D. at University of Chicago. At Atlantic Union College, South Lancaster, Massachusetts, he served as professor of history and academic dean. He was president of La Sierra College, then president of Loma Linda University, Loma Linda, California, from 1954 to 1967. Walla Walla College, Washington, conferred upon him the LL.D. degree in 1961. He is now Loma Linda University archivist and president emeritus. He has written three books: *Walk God's Battlefield*, *Outrider of the Apocalypse*, and *Dr. Edward Bancroft and the American Revolution*, besides eighty published articles.

OLIVER L. JACQUES (*chapters on Elmshaven and nineteenth-century medicine*) graduated from Columbia Union College, Washington, D.C., and has done graduate work at Andrews University and the University of Southern California. He has served as a missionary, church pastor, and hospital chaplain. He directed public relations at Battle Creek Sanitarium, Michigan, and university relations at Loma Linda University. For two years, he was administrative assistant to Congressman Jerry Pettis of California. He is now director of public relations at Kettering Medical Center, Kettering, Ohio. He has been active in numerous community service organizations and has written several books based on his experiences in Africa.

RICHARD W. SCHWARZ (*chapters on Battle Creek and the health-food industry*) received the M.S. and Ph.D. degrees from the University of Michigan. After teaching on the secondary level, he joined the faculty of Andrews University, Michigan, in 1955, and later became chairman of the department of history and political science there. His doctoral dissertation was entitled "John Harvey Kellogg, American Health Reformer." Southern Publishing Association published a popularized version, *John Harvey Kellogg, M.D.* in 1970. Schwarz holds membership in Phi Beta Kappa and Phi Alpha Theta. He is currently on leave preparing a college-level textbook in Seventh-day Adventist history.

RICHARD B. LEWIS (*chapters on Hinsdale and Saint Helena Sanitariums*) graduated from Pacific Union College in 1927. He received the M.A. degree at the University of Southern California and in 1949 the Ph.D. at Stanford University. He taught English and speech at Walla Walla and Pacific Union Colleges. He was associate book editor at Pacific Press, Mountain View, California, and academic dean at La Sierra College. Since 1967, he has been professor of English at Loma Linda University. He is author of two books: *Streams of Light* and *The Protestant Dilemma*. His interests include sound recording and color photography. His photographs have appeared on the covers of *This Week* and *Life and Health*.

ERIC WERE (*chapter on Australia and Sydney Sanitarium*) studied commercial art and advertising design at South Australia School of Arts, then worked as a commercial artist. After World War II he and his wife moved to New Guinea, where he managed a gold mine. While there, he began to write magazine articles and illustrate them with his own photographs. Leaving New Guinea, he embarked on a photography-writing career. He covered the visit of Queen Elizabeth II to Fiji for *Australian Women's Weekly*. In Vancouver, Canada, he again studied creative writing and ran a film business. He authored the book *Perilous Paradise* and has made documentary films of Christian missions endeavor on every continent except Antarctica.

FLOYD O. RITTENHOUSE (*chapters on Paradise Valley and Glendale Sanitariums*) graduated from Emmanuel Missionary College, later Andrews University, and received the M.A. and Ph.D. degrees at Ohio State University, Columbus. He taught history at Southern Missionary College, Tennessee, and Columbia Union College, Washington, D.C. He became dean and professor of history at Southern Missionary College, then held the same positions at Andrews University. He served as president of Andrews University from 1955 to 1963, and president of Pacific Union College from 1963 to 1972. Retired since 1972, Rittenhouse is working on a biographical project. He is a member of Phi Alpha Theta and a Rotarian.

W. FREDERICK NORWOOD (*chapters on Loma Linda*) graduated from Walla Walla College, Washington, and earned his M.A. and Ph.D. degrees at the University of Southern California. He served as registrar, associate dean, and dean of the College of Medical Evangelists (later Loma Linda University) School of Medicine, and as vice-president of the college. He was professor and chairman of the department of legal and cultural medicine from 1945 to 1970. His doctoral dissertation, *Medical Education in the United States Before the Civil War*, published in 1944 and reprinted in 1971, established him as a leading authority on the history of medical education. He has authored more than sixty articles in scientific and lay journals.

RICHARD H. UTT (*editor and coordinator*) graduated from Pacific Union College in 1945, earned the M.A. degree at Andrews University in 1958, and took additional graduate work at University of California, Berkeley. He served as a missionary in Central America and was president of the Costa Rica Mission of Seventh-day Adventists. Author of nearly 400 published articles, stories, and essays, he has been a contributing editor of *These Times* and assistant editor of *Signs of the Times*. He is author of three books: *A Century of Miracles*, *Harris and the Pines*, and *The Builders*. He was book editor at Pacific Press, Mountain View, California, from 1961 to 1976, and now is a free-lance writer and editor living in Wrightwood, California.

INDEX

Abbott, George K.   181, 182, 184, 185, *188*
Adelaide, Australia   128
Advent Review and Sabbath Herald   40, 45, 110, 184
Advertising, Kellogg Company   88, 89
Albany, New York   22
American Academy of Medicine   196
American Medical Association   25, 190, 196
American Medical Missionary College   96, 97, 100, 147, 148, 178, 192, 199
Andrews, John N.   43, *45*, 47
Andrews, Mrs. John N.   43
Andross, Mrs. Celian   *192*
Apothecaries   25
Arnold, William   127
Ashfield, Australia   127
Association of American Medical Colleges   190, 191
Atlantic City, New Jersey   180
Atwood, A. B.   110, 111
Australasian Union Conference   133
Australia   113, 114, 126-146
Australia, Ellen White in   12, 126-134
Avondale Health Retreat   *134*

Ballenger, E. W.   152, 153
Ballenger, J. F. and Mrs. J. F.   151, 152
Barnard, Len H.   133
Barnardo, Dr., of London   97
Barton, Clara   80
Bath girls, Battle Creek Sanitarium   *50*
Battle Creek, Michigan   12, 15, 23, 36-93, 140, 148, 170
Battle Creek College   51, 100, 110, 170, 195
Battle Creek Diet System Sterilized Bran   85
Battle Creek *Enquirer*   200
Battle Creek phobia   178
Battle Creek Pure Food Company   82
Battle Creek Sabbath School   108
Battle Creek Sanitarium   12, 36-73, *55*, *57*, *72*, *73*, 75-86, 100, 114, 127, 148, 178, 179, 200
Battle Creek Sanitarium, patronage graph   *73*
Battle Creek syndrome   178, 183
Battle Creek Toasted Corn Flake Company   83, 84
Beckwith home   97, 99, *104*
Bee, Maggie Hare   14
Bee, Mr.   14
Beechwood Cottage   *130*
Bellevue Hospital Medical College, New York   50, 96, 111
Berrien Springs, Michigan   17, 195
Bethany Rescue Home   131
Bigelow, Dr. Jacob   28
Bloomfield, Calif.   110
Boal, John E.   148
Body brace   35
Boilly, L., lithograph   *25*
Bourdeau, D.T.   110
Boyd, Dr. J.   26
Boyle, Dr. Robert   26
Boyle Avenue Dispensary   *200*

Boyle Heights, Los Angeles   195
Brand, Leslie C.   163, *164*, 169, 170
Brand Boulevard, Glendale   166
Braught, Dr. and Mrs. F.E.   131
British and Foreign Medical Review   26
Buffalo, New York   22
Burden, John A.   106, 113, *137*, 152, 160, 162, 163, *164*, 165, 167-171, 175ff, *179*, 200
Burden, Mrs. John A.   *137*
Burden Committee   167
Burke, Dr. W. P.   112
Butler, Lance L.   131
Butler, Lewis   131, *132*
Butler, Mrs. Lewis   *132*
Butterfield, Dr. A. D.   *157*
Butz, Florence   *115*

Caldwell, Dr. and Mrs. J. E.   131
California Conference   148, 179
California State Board of Medical Examiners   184, 190
Calomel   28
Caramel Cereal   140
Caramel Cereal Coffee   76, 80
Carnegie Foundation for the Advancement of Teaching   190
Caro, Dr. Edward R.   128
Carr Street Church, Los Angeles   179
Carter, A.   14
Cereal Flakes, first   76-78
Cero-Fruto   82
Chicago, Illinois   52, 53, 78, 95-100
Chicago Mission   97
Christchurch Sanitarium, New Zealand   131, *134*
Christian, L. H.   98
Civil War, American   44
Civil War Medicine   28
Coles, Dr. Larkin B.   40, 44
College of Medical Evangelists   100, 189ff
Colton, California   186, 189
Colwell, Dr. Nathan P.   190, 193, 196, *196*, 198
Comstock, Dr. Belle Wood   166
"Contagiousness of Puerperal Fever"   28
Cook, Algie   *115*
Cooranbong, Australia   127, 141
Corliss, J. O.   127
Cormack, A. W.   *142*
Coronado Hotel, San Diego   *150*
Corsets   34
Council on Medical Education   190, 191, 193, 198
Crisler, Clarence C.   14
Crystal Springs, California   110, 113
Crystal Springs Manor   *115*
Currow, Arthur   128
Currow, Louis   128

Davis, Andrew Jackson   26
Daniells, Arthur G.   16, 127, 150, 160, 169, 178, 185, 190, 194, *197*
Daumier, Honore   30

Davis, Ella "Puss"   80
Deer Park, California   170
Depression, Great   86
Detroit, Michigan   22, 52
Dickinson, Lansing   22
Disappointment of 1844   39
Dora Creek   141
Dougall, Dr. J. Park   184
Doutney, Mrs.   150
Drake, Fred   200
Drug store   *32*
Drugging   25-32, 51
Drugs   30

Eaton, Ella (Kellogg)   51, *52*, *71*, 76, 78
Eddy, Mary Baker   26
Electric belt   *34*
Electro-Hydropathic Institute   128
Elijah's Manna   *81*, 84
Elmwood Hall   99
Elmshaven   8-21, *8-21*, 113, 114, 131, 147, 170
Encyclopedia Britannica   25
Erie Canal   22
Escondido, California, church   153
Evans, I. H.   185
Evans, Dr. Newton G.   188, 192-199, *194*, *201*
Exercise at Battle Creek Sanitarium 38, 62-67
Exposition of Rational Medicine   28

Family Medical Advisor   26
Family Medical Chest Dispensatory   26
Fauchard, French dentist   25
Farnsworth, E. W.   130
Ferguson, Dave   171
Ferriar, John, M. D.   25
First Street Clinic, Los Angeles   191, 193, 19[?]
Fisher, George   140, 141, *142*
Flexner, Abraham   190, 191, *196*
Flint, Dr. Austin   50
Flint, Michigan   23
Footprints of Faith   95
Forbes, Sir John   26
Force cereal   82
Foreign Mission Board   15
Fox Valley, Australia   126
Frank Leslie's Illustrated Newspaper   13
Freeman, Dr. Margheurita   130, *136*, *138*

Gallup, Dr.   25
Gates, Edward H.   141
General Conference (and sessions)   14-16, 44, 46, 110, 112, 167, 176, 184 190, 193, 194
Gibbs, Dr. J. S.   112
Glen Haven Water Cure   44
Glendale, city   166, *166*, 167
Glendale High School   163
Gelndale Hotel   162, *163*
Glendale Sanitarium   160, 160-171, *168*, *169*
Good Health   51, 54

INDEX

Golden City 110
Good Samaritan Inn 99
Gospel Medical School 131
Gotzian, Josephine 150, *153*
Graham, Helen *14*
Graham, Dr. James 26
Graham, Sylvester 40, 44, 76, *76*
Granola 76, 140
Granose 113
Granose Flakes 78
Granose Grits 78
Granula 76
Grape-Nuts 76, 81
Graves, Judge Benjamin F. 47
Great Cereal Boom 81, 86, *87*
Greeley, Horace 30

Hahnemann and homeopathy 26
Hair restorer *35*
Hall, Mrs., matron at Battle Creek 96
Halsey, E. C. 140
Hamilton, Salem 146, 152, *157*
Hammond, Dr. William A., 28
Hanson-Pickett, Mamie *117*
Hare, Dr. George 196
Harrison, Dr. T. H. 147, 148, 150
Hartland Center, Michigan 23
Harvard University 190
Haskell, Mrs. Stephen N. 181, 197
Haskell, Stephen N. 127, 153, 181, 194
Hatzfeldhaven Hansenide Hospital 133
Healey, William M. 111, 153
Health food industry 74-93, *74-93*, 113, 114, *120*, 140-145, *142-145*, 152
Health Home, Christchurch, N. Z. 131
Health Reformer 30, 46, 50, 170
Helping Hand Laundry 131
Helping Hand Mission 131
Helping Hand Wood Yard 131, *134*
Hilliard Family 39
Hickox, Pastor and Mrs., and daughter *133*
Hinsdale Sanitarium 94-105, *104, 105*
Hinsdale Sanitarium and Benevolent Association 98
History of Glendale and Vicinity 165
Hogue, Mable *165*
Holmes, Oliver Wendell 28
Home Handbook 58, *59*
Homeopathy 26, *33*
Horner, Helen *156*
Horner, Zoe *156*
Howell, Warren E. 181, 182, 184, *188*
Howell Mountain 113, 115, 170, 201
Hoyt, H. E. 98
Hubbard, Lizzie 128
Hygieo-Therapeutic Institute 49, 108 (See also Trall, Dr. Russell T.)

Jackson, Charles 28
Jackson, Dr. James Caleb 39, 40, 44, 76
Jacques, Mrs. Grace *17*
James, Effie *14*
Janeway, Dr. Edward G. 50
Johns Hopkins University 190

Johnson, I. O. 152
Johnson, Dr. Sophie 148

Kellogg, Ann 23, *23*, 30, 77
Kellogg brothers 113, 200
Kellogg, Clara 77
Kellogg Company 83, 85, *92, 93*
Kellogg, Ella 51, *52, 71*, 76, 78
Kellogg, Dr. John Harvey 14, 15, 34, 35, 36, 48, *48*, 49-86, *52, 66-71, 77, 84*, 96, 98, 110, 111, 140, 148, 170, 178, 200, 201
Kellogg John Preston 22, 23, *23*, 25, 30, 46-49
Kellogg, Laura 77
Kellogg, Mary 22
Kellogg, Dr. Merritt 22, 49, 108, 110, 111, *111*, 131, *133*
Kellogg, Mrs. Merritt *111*, 131, *133*
Kellogg, Preston S. 77
Kellogg, "Professor" Frank 84
Kellogg, Will K. *74*, 75-86, *77, 79, 80, 85*, 100, 108, 170, 200, 201
Kellogg, Smith Moses 22
Kellogg's Bran 85
Kellogg's Sterilized Bran 85
Kellogg's Toasted Corn Flakes 84, 85
Kelly, Dr. Howard 52
Kress, Dr. Daniel H. 130, *136*, 171
Kress, Dr. Lauretta 130, *136*
Kimbell, C. B. 97
Kimlin, C. E. 169
King, Annie 115

Lacey, Lenora 164
Ladies' Home Journal 13, 84
Lamson, Dr. Phoebe 43, 47
LaVita Inn 81
Laws of Life, The 43
Lawsuit between Kellogg brothers 85
Lay, Dr. H. S. 43-49, *47*
Learned, Mr. and Mrs. 171
Lewis, C. C. 171
Life Boat Home for Girls 97
Life Boat Magazine 100, 171
Life Boat mission 96
Life Boat Rescue Home 99
Lindsay, Harmon 166
Lindsay, Dr. Kate 47
Lindsay, Winifred 166
Living Temple, The 53, 178
Lloyd, Ernest 170, *170*
Lobingier, Dr. Andrew S. 164
Loma Linda, California 12, 173-201
Loma Linda church *200*
Loma Linda College of Evangelists 181ff
Loma Linda Hotel 175
Loma Linda Sanitarium *174*, 180-187, 192
"Lonesome Linda" 175, 199
Long, Dr. Crawford 28
Los Angeles camp meeting 148
Los Angeles County Hospital 192, 199
Los Angeles *Times* 179
Loughborough, John N. 45, 46-49, 108, 110
Lydia Pinkham's Female Compound 13

Madison Sanitarium 192-195
Madison, Tennessee 195
Magan, Dr. Lillian 192
Magan, Dr. Percy T. 17, 100, *188*, 189-198, *197, 210*
Magan, Mrs. Wellesley 192
"The Magnates" 194
Malta Vita 82
Malted Nuts 80
Malted Oats 82
Mapl-Flakes 82
Marvin, Chaplain 171
Mason, Paul *14*
Mayo Brothers Clinic 86
McCutcheon, James T., cartoon by *87*
McDonald, Mrs. Esther *135*
Meaford cottage 127
Medical Education in the United States and Canada 190
Medical Histories and Reflections 25
Medical Reserve Corps 196
Menu, Loma Linda Hotel *176*
Merrill, Mrs. *165*
Michigan Conference 46
Michigan legislature 47
Miller, Dr. Harry 170
Miller, William 39
Millerites 39
Moore, Zach, on C. W. Post 86
Morrison, John 111
Morse, G. W. 141
Morse, Dr. J. F. *105*
Morton, William 28
Mound City, California 176
Mound City Hotel 176
Mountain View, California 185
Munson, R. W. *14*
Murfett, Mr. 130
Musgrave, Dr. W. E. 198

Napa, California 112
Napa County, California 12
Napa Valley, 111, 115
National Religious Liberty Association 15
Nethery, J. J. 168
New Zealand 131, 141
New Zealand Adventist Hospital 131
Norka 82
Noncombatancy 196
Northampton, Massachusetts 22
Northwestern University, Illinois 96
North American Division 193
Nut Cero 114
Nut Loaf 114
Nuttose 79

Oakland, California 110, 111
Occidental College 197
Old Folks' Home and Orphanage 131
Orphans, Chicago area *102, 103*
Otis, General Harrison Gray, daughter of 179
Otsego, Michigan, health vision 39
Our Home on the Hillside *42, 43*, 44

INDEX

Owen, R. S.   177

Pacific Health Journal   112, *113*
Pacific Islands   133
Pacific Medical Missionary Association   150
Pacific Press   111, 112
Pacific Union Conference   179, 181, 185
Pacific Union Conference Committee   167, 177
Pacific Union Recorder   113
Pallant, Mary   128
Panama Isthmus   110
Paradise Valley Sanitarium   146-159, *146, 158, 159,* 175, 177, 179
Palmer, E. R.   151, 152
Palmer, Mrs. E. R.   151
Pasteur, Louis   30
Patent medicines   30
Patin, Dr. Guy   *31*
Paulson, Dr. David   94, 95-101, *99,* 161, 170, 171, 190, 194, 200
Paulson, Dr. Mary   94, 95-101, *99, 105,* 200
Paulson, Nels   98
Payne, William   *157*
Peanut butter, invention of   79
Pep cereal   85
Perkey, Henry   77
Phrenology   *34*
Physician, as Jack-of-all-trades   *24*
Physician, country   *27*
Physicians, in consultation   *25*
Physician's shingle   *24*
Pitcairn ship   114, 131
Post, Charles W.   80-86, *81,* 171
Post food factory   82
Postum   81
Potts, Dr. Anna Mary   147, *153,* 155
Potts Sanitarium   147, 148
Powell, Horace B. quoted   201
Pratt, William A.   110, 111, *111*
Priessnitz   35
Protose   79

Quaker Oats   82
Quimby, Phineas   26

Rand, Dr. Howard F.   171
Rational Hydrotherapy   51
Redlands, California   175, 177, 179
Redlands University   197
Reeves, Minnie   135
Rescue Home   131
Residence, The   70
Review and Herald (see also *Advent Review and Sabbath Herald*)   40, 45, 110, 184
Review and Herald Publishing Association   78
Rice, C. E.   *157*
Rice, J. D.   112
Richardson, F. I.   152
Rising Star   110
Risley, Dr. Edward H.   *188, 189,* 199
Riverside, California   175
Robinson, Dores E.   *14*

Ruble, Dr. W. A.   185, *188,* 189-192
Rudge, William F.   *135*
Rural Health Retreat   109, 111-115, *115-125*
Rural Health Retreat Association   111
Russell, Dr. William   50
Rutherford, California   110

Saint Helena, California   12, 108, 110, *112*
Saint Helena Hospital and Health Center   115
Saint Helena Sanitarium (see also Rural Health Retreat)   108-125, *109, 115-125,* 160, 179
Saint Hilda's Hall   163, *163*
Salisbury, Wilbur D.   193
Sanitarium Health Food Agency (Australia)   140
Sanitarium Health Food Company (Australia)   141
San Bernardino County Hospital   192
San Diego, California   147, 148, *149-151*
San Francisco, California   108, 110
San Pasqual, California, church   153
Santa Rosa, California   110, 111
Sanitas Company   78ff
Santee, Clarence   163, 164, 171
Saturday Evening Post   13
Science and Health   26
Scott, Henry L.   127
Semmens, A. W.   127, *129*
Semmens, Mrs. A. W.   127, *129*
"Sermon in a Time Table"   61
Sharp, F. L.   128
Shaver, Naomi C.   *165*
Shepard, Will   74
Sherer, John C.   *165*
Shredded Whole Wheat Bread   77
Shryock, Dr. Alfred Q.   195
Signs of the Times   110, 111
Simmons, George H.   196
Simpson, Dr. Abbie Winegar   164
Smith, Uriah   45, 48, 49
Somo   76
Sopas Adventist Hospital   133
South Dakota   95, 96
South Seas   114
Southern California Conference   148, 150, 155, 156, 163, 179-184
Spalding, Arthur W.   *14,* 170
Spring Street, Los Angeles   162
Steel, Mimie   128
Steps to Christ   12
Stewart, Mary   *14*
Student Army Training Corps   197
Summer Hill, Australia   127, 128, 131
Summer Hill Sanitarium   140
"Sunnyside" residence   127
Sutherland, Dr. Edward A.   193, 195, 197
Switzerland, J. N. Andrews in   110
Sydney, Australia   127
Sydney Sanitarium   114, 126, *126,* 130, 133, *139*

Taft, President William H.   170

Taylor, Lena   *115*
"Temple of Health," London   26
Texas, Battle Creek Sanitarium promotion in   171
Thomason, Dr. George   170, 192, *201*
Threadville, Michigan   23
Towers Addition, Battle Creek Sanitarium   *72, 73*
Trall, Dr. Russell, T.   39, 40, 44, 49-51, 108
Tyrone Township, Michigan   23

Ulrich, Carl   128
Ulrich, Mrs. Julia   153
Union College   185
University of Michigan Medical College   96
University of Southern California School of Medicine   198
University of Tennessee   192, 195

Van Horn, I. D.   110
Van Houten, Mrs.   98
Vehicles, Kellogg Company   *90, 91*

Waggoner, Dr. Ellet J.   111, 112
Waggoner, J. H.   112
Wahroonga   130
Wailing, Mae   *14*
Walker, Thomas   26
Warburton Sanitarium and Hospital   131
Washington, D. C.   53
Washington, George   25
Water-Cure, The   41
Wayside Diagnosis   *29*
Wessels, John   128
Wessels brothers   96
West Hinsdale, Illinois   97
Western Health Reform Institute (see also Battle Creek Sanitarium)   43, 46, *46,* 47, 48, 49, 50, 76, 110
White, Arthur L., quoted   195
White, Ellen G., home at Elmshaven   8-21; pictured *8, 11, 13, 14, 186, 187;* see individual chapters for Mrs. White's activities and counsels relative to the various institutions.
White, Henry   44
White, James   13, 40, 44, 45, *45,* 46-52, 108-110
White, Dr. Julia   181
White, W. C.   *14,* 44, 127, 152, 153, 176, 178, 184, 190
White family portrait   *13*
White Memorial Hospital   197, 200
Whitelock, Dr. T. S.   147-151, *153,* 154
Whitelock, Mrs. T. S.   147, 148, *153*
Whitelock, T. S., Jr.   154
Wild, Mary (Paulson)   96
Williams, Hannah   *135*
Woodbury, Tessie   *14*
World War II   196

Yountville, California, camp meeting   110

Zo cereal   85